Advanced
Modular
Mathematics

D0480763

MECHANICS 2

Graham Smithers

SECOND EDITION

COLLINS

nec
NATIONAL
EXTENSION
COLLEGE

Unit M2

Published by HarperCollins Publishers Limited
77–85 Fulham Palace Road
Hammersmith
London W6 8JB

www.CollinsEducation.com
On-line Support for Schools and Colleges

© National Extension College Trust Ltd 2000
First published 2000
ISBN 000 322516 X

This book was written by Graham Smithers for the National Extension College Trust Ltd.

British Library Cataloguing in Publication Data
A catalogue record for this publication is available from the British Library.

Original internal design: Derek Lee
Cover design and implementation: Terry Bambrook
Project editors: Hugh Hillyard-Parker and Margaret Levin
Page layout: Stephen Pargeter
Printed and bound: Scotprint, Musselburgh

The authors and publishers thank Dave Wilkins for his comments on this book.

The National Extension College is an educational trust and a registered charity with a distinguished body of trustees. It is an independent, self-financing organisation.

Since it was established in 1963, NEC has pioneered the development of flexible learning for adults. NEC is actively developing innovative materials and systems for distance-learning options from basic skills and general education to degree and professional training.

For further details of NEC resources that support Advanced Modular Mathematics, and other NEC courses, contact NEC Customer Services:

National Extension College Trust Ltd
18 Brooklands Avenue
Cambridge CB2 2HN
Telephone 01223 316644, Fax 01223 313586
Email resources@nec.ac.uk, Home page www.nec.ac.uk

You might also like to visit:

www.fireandwater.com
The book lover's website

UNIT

M2
Contents

M2

M2

Advanced Modular Mathematics

FOREWORD This book is one of a series covering the Edexcel Advanced Subsidiary (AS) and Advanced GCE in Mathematics. It covers all the subject material for Mechanics 2 (Unit M2), examined from 2001 onwards.

While this series of text books has been structured to match the Edexcel specification, we hope that the informal style of the text and approach to important concepts will encourage other readers whose final exams are from other Boards to use the books for extra reading and practice. In particular, we have included references to the OCR syllabus (see below).

This book is meant to be *used*: read the text, study the worked examples and work through the Practice questions and Summary exercises, which will give you practice in the basic skills you need for maths at this level. Many exercises, and worked examples, are based on applications of the mathematics in this book. There are many books for advanced mathematics, which include many more exercises: use this book to direct your studies, making use of as many other resources as you can.

There are many features in this book that you will find particularly useful:

- Each **section** covers one discrete area of the new Edexcel specification. The order of topics is exactly the same as in the specification.

- **Practice questions** are given at regular intervals throughout each section. The questions are graded to help you build up your mathematical skills gradually through the section. The **Answers** to these questions come at the end of the relevant section.

- **Summary exercises** are given at the end of each section; these include more full-blown, exam-type questions. Full, worked solutions are given in a separate **Solutions** section at the end of the book.

- In addition, we have provided a complete **Practice examination paper**, which you can use as a 'dummy run' of the actual exam when you reach the end of your studies on M2.

- Alongside most of the headings in this book you will see boxed references, e.g. $\boxed{\text{OCR } \mathbf{M2}\ 5.8.1\ (a)}$ These are for students following the OCR specification and indicate which part of that specification the topic covers.

- Key Skills: because of the nature of mechanics, your work on this book will not provide many obvious opportunities for gathering evidence of Key Skills, and so we have not included any Key Skills references (as we have done in other books in this series).

The National Extension College has more experience of flexible-learning materials than any other body (see p. ii). This series is a distillation of that experience: Advanced Modular Mathematics helps to put you in control of your own learning.

1

Kinematics of a particle

INTRODUCTION If you throw a ball straight up in the air, you can use the formulae in Section 2 of Unit M1 to work out how high it will go. But if you don't throw it straight up, and throw it at an angle instead (as in cricket), how high will it reach then? In this section we'll find out how to answer that question.

In real life, of course, the wind will be blowing so that the cricket ball will be buffeted by variable air streams. The forces acting on the ball will therefore not be constant and so neither will its acceleration. Hence, since we cannot use the five constant acceleration equations, a totally new approach is required. This involves calculus – differentiation and integration – and in this section we'll be looking at some examples of variable acceleration.

When you have finished this section you should be able to:

● solve projectile problems (in a vertical plane under gravity)
● use the calculus to work out formulae for displacement, velocity and acceleration.

Vertical motion under gravity

OCR M1 5.7.4 (b)

We saw in Section 2 of Unit M1 that:

● the following formulae are useful when solving questions involving a constant acceleration:

$$v = u + at, \quad s = \left(\frac{u+v}{2}\right) t, \quad v^2 = u^2 + 2as, \quad s = ut + \frac{1}{2} at^2, \quad s = vt - \frac{1}{2} at^2$$

● the acceleration due to gravity, g, is usually taken as 9.8 m s^{-2}.

We also saw how to use this information to model questions involving vertical motion under gravity. Let's remind ourselves about such questions.

Example A cricket ball is projected vertically downwards from the top of a tower with a velocity of 30 m s^{-1}, and takes 4 seconds to reach the ground. What is the height of the tower?

Solution

$\downarrow$:	u	v	a	s	t
	30		9.8	?	4

(The arrow $\downarrow$ indicates the direction of flight.)

$\therefore \quad s = ut + \frac{1}{2} at^2 \quad \Rightarrow s = 120 + 78.4 \quad \Rightarrow s = 198.4$

$\therefore \quad$ The tower is 198.4 m high.

Example	A projectile is projected vertically upwards with an initial velocity of 30 m s^{-1}. Two seconds later, another particle is projected upwards with an initial velocity of 25 m s^{-1}. When are the two particles at the same height?
Solution	The first particle gives us:

↑: u v a s t
    30   –9.8 T

(where T is the time that the particle has been flying).

The second particle is therefore given by:

↑: u v a s t
    25   –9.8 $T-2$

(The second particle has been flying for two seconds less than the first particle.)

Using $s = ut + \frac{1}{2}at^2$ for both particles, they will be at the same height when:

$$30T - 4.9T^2 = 25(T-2) - 4.9(T-2)^2$$
$$\Rightarrow \quad 30T - 4.9T^2 = 25(T-2) - 4.9(T^2 - 4T + 4)$$
$$\Rightarrow \quad 69.6 = 14.6T \quad \Rightarrow \quad T = 4.77$$

∴   The particles will be at the same height 4.77 seconds after the projection of the first particle (or 2.77 seconds after the projection of the second particle).

Practice questions A

(Take $g = 9.8$ m s^{-2} as required.)

1 A pebble falls off a shelf 2 m high. How long will it take to fall?

2 An airgun pellet is fired vertically upwards at 73.5 m s^{-1}. How high does it rise?

3 A ball is thrown vertically upwards at 10 m s^{-1} and caught at the same height. For how long is it in the air?

4 A stone is catapulted vertically upwards at 12 m s^{-1}. For how long does its height exceed 5 m?

5 How long does it take a ball to fall vertically from rest through 40 m?

6 A stone is thrown vertically upward from ground level at 7 m s^{-1}. Find:
   (a) the height to which the stone rises
   (b) the time to reach the greatest height
   (c) the total time the stone is in the air

7 A particle is projected vertically upward from the ground with a velocity of 14.7 m s^{-1}. What time elapses before it reaches the ground again?

8 A sandbag is dropped over the side of an observation balloon at a moment when it is ascending vertically at 3 m s^{-1}. The sandbag is observed to hit the ground 9 seconds later. What deduction would the observer make concerning the height when the sandbag was dropped over?

9 A ball is dropped from a height of 10 m onto a concrete floor and rebounds with a speed 0.7 times the downward speed on arrival. Find the height reached from the rebound.

10 Two rockets are fired vertically from launching pads side by side. The first rocket moves vertically upwards with an acceleration of $6g$ and the second with an acceleration of $8g$. If the second rocket is fired 1 second after the first, find how long after its launching the second rocket overtakes the first.

11 A particle is projected vertically upwards, from the point B, with speed 30 m s^{-1}. The time taken to return to B is T seconds. Ignoring air resistance, find T.

The point P is d metres vertically above B. Given the particle is above P for $\frac{1}{4}T$ seconds, find d.

How to tackle projectile problems in two dimensions   OCR M2 5.8.3 (a),(b)

Begin by writing down $u \ v \ a \ s \ t$ in the two directions, one horizontally and one vertically.

$\therefore \ \rightarrow: \quad u \quad v \quad a \quad s \quad t \qquad$ and $\uparrow: \quad u \quad v \quad a \quad s \quad t$

Horizontally there is no acceleration and so the u and v in that direction must always be the same. Vertically the acceleration will be -9.8 m s^{-2}. The times in the vertical table will be exactly the same as the times in the horizontal table:

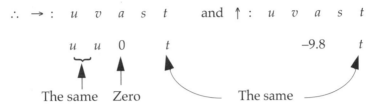

That gives you the general approach to take, except that if you want to find the direction in which a projectile is moving, you get its two velocity components and work from that:

Figure 1.1

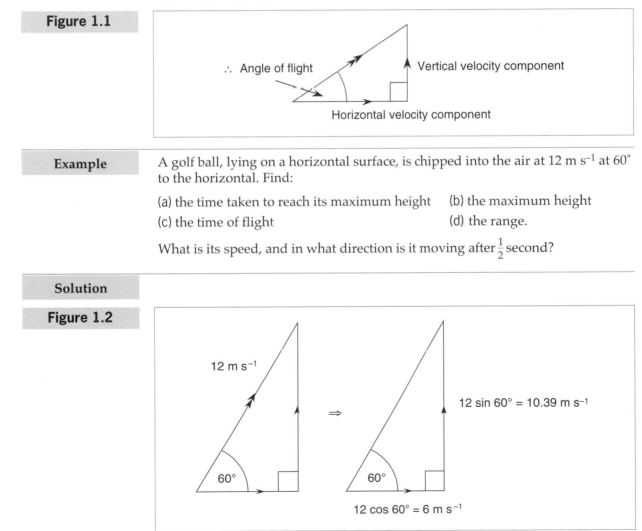

Example

A golf ball, lying on a horizontal surface, is chipped into the air at 12 m s^{-1} at 60° to the horizontal. Find:

(a) the time taken to reach its maximum height   (b) the maximum height
(c) the time of flight   (d) the range.

What is its speed, and in what direction is it moving after $\frac{1}{2}$ second?

Solution

Figure 1.2

(Check with Unit M1, Section 4, if you've forgotten how to resolve.)

$\therefore \; \rightarrow : \quad u \quad v \quad a \quad s \quad t \qquad$ and $\uparrow : \qquad u \quad v \quad a \quad s \quad t$
$\qquad\qquad 6 \quad 6 \quad 0 \quad ? \quad ? \qquad\qquad\qquad 10.39 \quad -9.8 \quad ? \quad ?$

(a) The ball reaches maximum height when $\uparrow v = 0$.

$\therefore$ Using $v = u + at \Rightarrow 0 = 10.39 - 9.8t \Rightarrow t = 1.06$

$\therefore$ The ball takes 1.06 seconds to reach maximum height.

(A practical tip: in tackling numerical questions, write down suitably rounded figures so that your methods are clear but, at the same time, use the memories in your calculator to get as accurate answers as possible. Once you've got an answer, round it off sensibly but, once again, keep the 'correct' answer in one of the memories.)

(b) To find the maximum height we want $\uparrow s$.

$\therefore$ Using $s = \left(\dfrac{u + v}{2}\right)t \Rightarrow s = \left(\dfrac{10.39 + 0}{2}\right)1.06 = 5.5$

$\therefore$ The maximum height is 5.5 m.

(c) It takes as long to go up as it takes to come down.

$\therefore$ Its time of flight $= 2 \times 1.06 = 2.12$ seconds

(d) To find the range we want $\rightarrow s$.

$\therefore$ Using $s = \left(\dfrac{u + v}{2}\right)t \Rightarrow s = \left(\dfrac{6 + 6}{2}\right)2.12 = 12.7$

$\therefore$ Its range is 12.7 m.

After $\frac{1}{2}$ second, its $\uparrow v$ is given by $v = 10.39 - (9.8 \times \frac{1}{2}) = 5.49$ m s^{-1}

Since $\rightarrow v$ is always 6 m s^{-1} we therefore have:

Figure 1.3

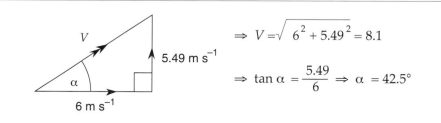

$\Rightarrow V = \sqrt{6^2 + 5.49^2} = 8.1$

$\Rightarrow \tan \alpha = \dfrac{5.49}{6} \Rightarrow \alpha = 42.5°$

$\therefore$ After $\frac{1}{2}$ second it is moving at 8.1 m s^{-1} at 42.5° to the horizontal (correct to 1 d.p.)

Example

An emergency relief aircraft releases its parcel of food supplies when descending at 20 m s^{-1} at an angle 30° to the horizontal. The parcel strikes the target 5 seconds later. At what height is the parcel released, and how far does the parcel travel horizontally?

Comment on the mathematical model that was used to solve this problem and name one factor that was ignored, but which would affect the result.

| Solution | Look at the following diagram. |

Figure 1.4

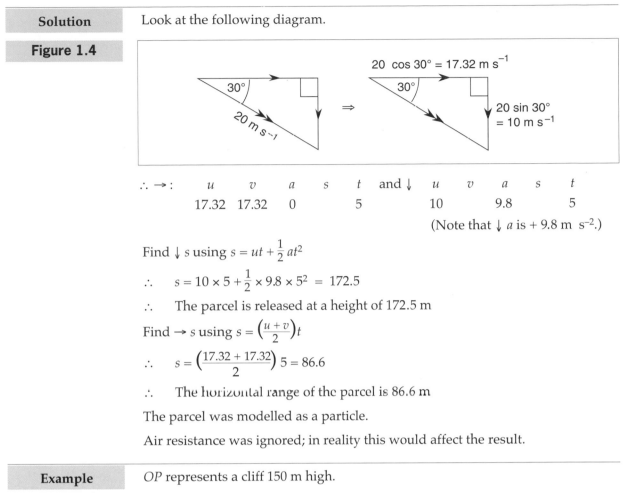

$$\therefore \ \rightarrow : \quad \begin{array}{ccccc} u & v & a & s & t \\ 17.32 & 17.32 & 0 & & 5 \end{array} \quad \text{and} \downarrow \quad \begin{array}{ccccc} u & v & a & s & t \\ 10 & & 9.8 & & 5 \end{array}$$

(Note that $\downarrow a$ is $+ 9.8$ m s^{-2}.)

Find $\downarrow s$ using $s = ut + \dfrac{1}{2} at^2$

$\therefore \quad s = 10 \times 5 + \dfrac{1}{2} \times 9.8 \times 5^2 \ = \ 172.5$

$\therefore$ The parcel is released at a height of 172.5 m

Find $\rightarrow s$ using $s = \left(\dfrac{u + v}{2} \right) t$

$\therefore \quad s = \left(\dfrac{17.32 + 17.32}{2} \right) 5 = 86.6$

$\therefore$ The horizontal range of the parcel is 86.6 m

The parcel was modelled as a particle.

Air resistance was ignored; in reality this would affect the result.

| Example | *OP* represents a cliff 150 m high. |

Figure 1.5

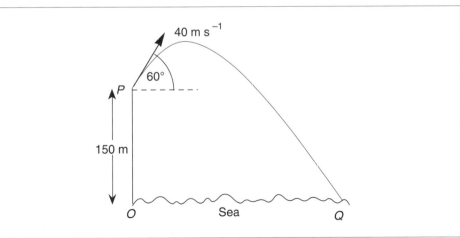

A ball is thrown from *P* with velocity 40 m s^{-1} at 60° to the horizontal. Find:

(a)   the greatest height of the ball above the sea

(b)   the time taken to hit the sea

(c)   the range *OQ*

(d)   the velocity at *Q*, in magnitude and direction.

Solution

First the useful diagram.

Figure 1.6

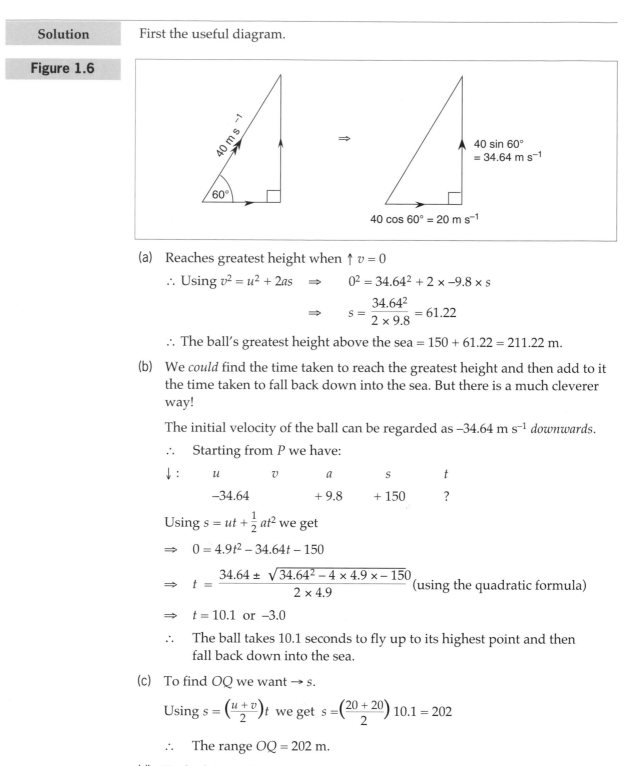

(a)   Reaches greatest height when $\uparrow v = 0$

∴ Using $v^2 = u^2 + 2as$ ⇒ $0^2 = 34.64^2 + 2 \times -9.8 \times s$

⇒ $s = \dfrac{34.64^2}{2 \times 9.8} = 61.22$

∴ The ball's greatest height above the sea $= 150 + 61.22 = 211.22$ m.

(b)   We *could* find the time taken to reach the greatest height and then add to it the time taken to fall back down into the sea. But there is a much cleverer way!

The initial velocity of the ball can be regarded as -34.64 m s^{-1} *downwards*.

∴   Starting from P we have:

$\downarrow$:	u	v	a	s	t
	-34.64		$+9.8$	$+150$	?

Using $s = ut + \dfrac{1}{2}at^2$ we get

⇒ $0 = 4.9t^2 - 34.64t - 150$

⇒ $t = \dfrac{34.64 \pm \sqrt{34.64^2 - 4 \times 4.9 \times - 150}}{2 \times 4.9}$ (using the quadratic formula)

⇒ $t = 10.1$ or -3.0

∴   The ball takes 10.1 seconds to fly up to its highest point and then fall back down into the sea.

(c)   To find OQ we want $\rightarrow s$.

Using $s = \left(\dfrac{u+v}{2}\right)t$ we get $s = \left(\dfrac{20+20}{2}\right)10.1 = 202$

∴   The range $OQ = 202$ m.

(d)   To find $\downarrow v$ at Q we can use $v = u + at$

∴ $v = -34.64 + 9.8 \times 10.1$ (see table in (b))

∴ $v = 64.34$

Since $\rightarrow v$ is always 20 m s^{-1} we have at Q:

Figure 1.7

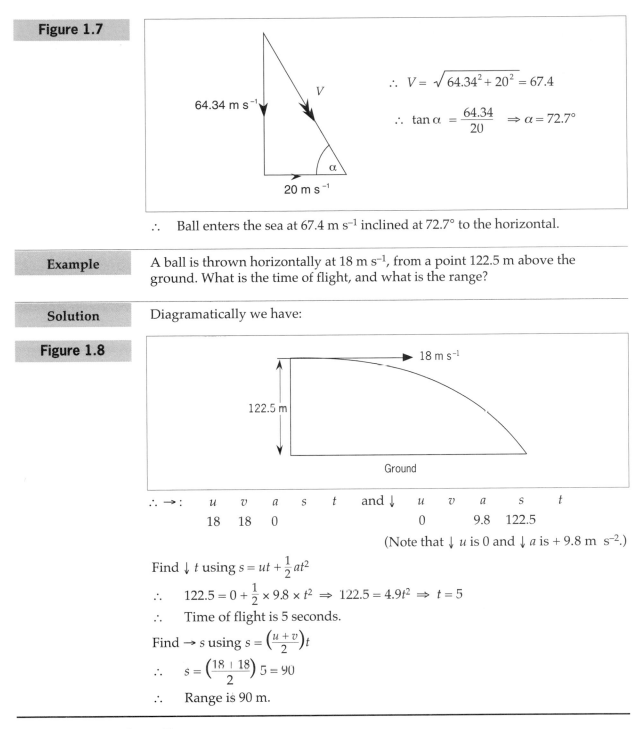

$$\therefore \quad V = \sqrt{64.34^2 + 20^2} = 67.4$$

$$\therefore \quad \tan \alpha = \frac{64.34}{20} \implies \alpha = 72.7°$$

∴ Ball enters the sea at 67.4 m s⁻¹ inclined at 72.7° to the horizontal.

Example

A ball is thrown horizontally at 18 m s⁻¹, from a point 122.5 m above the ground. What is the time of flight, and what is the range?

Solution

Diagramatically we have:

Figure 1.8

∴ →:	u	v	a	s	t	and ↓	u	v	a	s	t
	18	18	0				0		9.8	122.5	

(Note that ↓ u is 0 and ↓ a is + 9.8 m s⁻².)

Find ↓ t using $s = ut + \frac{1}{2} at^2$

$\therefore \quad 122.5 = 0 + \frac{1}{2} \times 9.8 \times t^2 \implies 122.5 = 4.9t^2 \implies t = 5$

∴ Time of flight is 5 seconds.

Find → s using $s = \left(\frac{u+v}{2}\right)t$

$\therefore \quad s = \left(\frac{18 + 18}{2}\right) 5 = 90$

∴ Range is 90 m.

Practice questions B

(Take $g = 9.8$ m s⁻² as required.)

1 John stands on a vertical cliff's edge and throws a ball horizontally out to sea.

When the ball leaves John's hand it is 80 m above sea level. Ignoring air resistance, find the time that elapses before the ball falls into the sea. If he throws it with a horizontal velocity of 15 m s⁻¹, how far from the foot of the cliff does the ball fall?

2 A bowler delivers a ball horizontally at 30 m s⁻¹, his hand being 2 m above the ground. How far from him does the ball pitch (i.e. hit the ground), and what is the time of flight?

3 At a range of 200 m, a bullet fired horizontally strikes the target 0.2 m below the point at which the rifle pointed. Find the initial velocity of the bullet.

4 A tennis ball is served horizontally from a height of 2.3 m and it strikes the ground at a point 28 m away from the server. Find its height when it passes the net 12 m from the server.

5 A batsman hits a ball at 70° with the horizontal, the ball leaving the bat at 32 m s⁻¹. The boundary is 75 m away. Does he succeed or fail in scoring a six, and how far from the boundary line does the ball bounce?

6 A ball runs down a roof inclined at 45° to the horizontal and leaves the edge at 5 m s⁻¹. The ball strikes the ground 5 m away from the vertical wall of the building. Find the height of the edge of the roof above the ground.

7 A ball projected horizontally from the top of a vertical cliff 30 m high, strikes the sea 25 m from the foot of the cliff. Find the velocity of projection and the velocity of the ball at the instant of striking the sea.

8

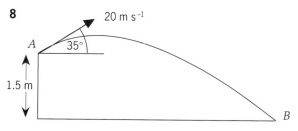

A batsman hits a cricket ball, giving it a speed of 20 m s⁻¹ at an angle of elevation of 35° The point *A* where he hits the ball is 1.5 m above the ground, which is horizontal. The ball then moves freely under gravity and hits the ground at the point *B* (see diagram). By modelling the ball as a particle and ignoring air resistance, find:

(a) the time taken by the ball to travel from *A* to *B*,

(b) the horizontal distance of *B* from *A*, giving your answers correct to 3 s.f.

9

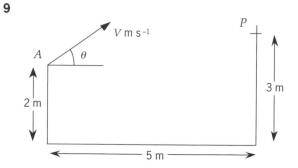

Shirley is throwing a ball at a vertical wall and trying to hit a point *P* marked on that wall and 3 m above the ground. The ball leaves Shirley's hand at point *A* which is 2 m above the ground (see diagram). The speed with which the ball leaves Shirley's hand is *V* m s⁻¹ inclined at an angle θ to the horizontal.

(a) When $V = 9$ and $\theta = 50°$, the ball hits the wall at *Q*. Find whether the ball is rising or falling at *Q*, and find the distance *PQ*.

(b) When $\theta = 40°$, find the value of *V* for which the ball hits the wall at *P*.

10 A ball is projected from a point on horizontal ground. The speed of projection is 35 m s⁻¹ and the greatest height reached is 25 m. Assuming no air resistance, find the angle of projection above the horizontal and the speed of the ball as it passes through the highest point.

11 A cricket ball is thrown from a point *P*, with a speed of 30 m s⁻¹ and at an angle 35° above the horizontal. After 2.5 seconds the ball is at *Q*. Ignoring air resistance, find the magnitude and direction of the velocity of the ball as it passes through *Q*.

12 A ball is projected from a point *P*, with speed *V* m s⁻¹ at an angle of θ above the horizontal. After 5 seconds the horizontal component of the velocity of the ball is 25 m s⁻¹ and the vertical component is 10 m s⁻¹ downwards. The effect of air resistance may be ignored.

(a) Find the values of *V* and θ.

(b) The highest point on the ball's path is *d* metres above the level of *P*. Find *d*.

Tackling projectile questions algebraically

In your examination you may be expected to derive general formulae for greatest height, time of flight and range. Let's see how this might be done.

| Example | For the projectile illustrated below, prove that: |

(a) the time of flight is $\dfrac{2u \sin \alpha}{g}$

(b) the greatest height reached is $\dfrac{u^2 \sin^2 \alpha}{2g}$

(c) the range is $\dfrac{2u^2 \sin \alpha \cos \alpha}{g}$

Figure 1.8

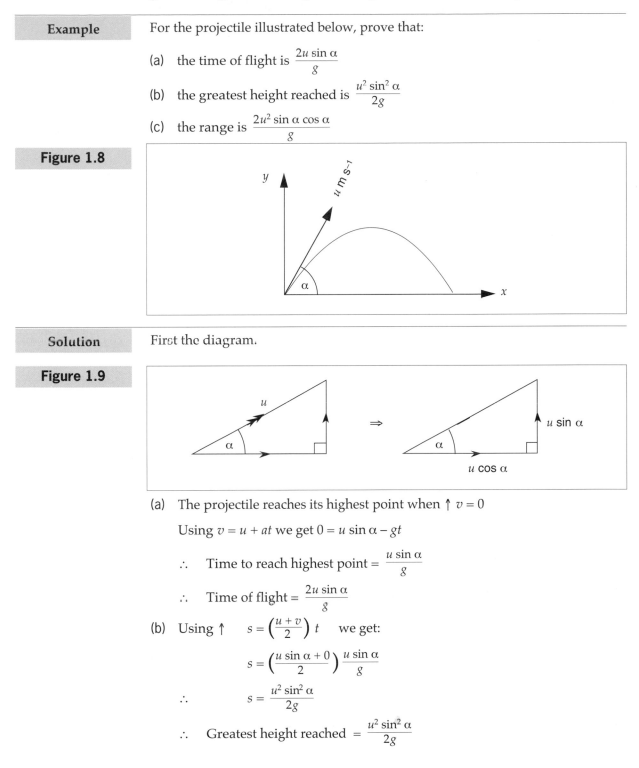

Solution

First the diagram.

Figure 1.9

(a) The projectile reaches its highest point when $\uparrow v = 0$

Using $v = u + at$ we get $0 = u \sin \alpha - gt$

∴ Time to reach highest point $= \dfrac{u \sin \alpha}{g}$

∴ Time of flight $= \dfrac{2u \sin \alpha}{g}$

(b) Using ↑ $s = \left(\dfrac{u + v}{2}\right) t$ we get:

$$s = \left(\frac{u \sin \alpha + 0}{2}\right) \frac{u \sin \alpha}{g}$$

∴ $\qquad s = \dfrac{u^2 \sin^2 \alpha}{2g}$

∴ Greatest height reached $= \dfrac{u^2 \sin^2 \alpha}{2g}$

(c) Using → $s = \left(\dfrac{u+v}{2}\right) t$ we get:

$$s = \left(\dfrac{u\cos\alpha + u\cos\alpha}{2}\right) \dfrac{2u\sin\alpha}{g}$$

$$\therefore \qquad s = \dfrac{2u^2\sin\alpha\cos\alpha}{g}$$

$\therefore$ The range is given by $\dfrac{2u^2\sin\alpha\cos\alpha}{g}$

$\left(\text{If you go on to study Unit P2, you will see there that } 2\sin\alpha\cos\alpha \text{ can be more}\right.$
simply written as $\sin 2\alpha$. This means that the range is also given by
$\left. \dfrac{u^2\sin 2\alpha}{g}.\right)$

Before you take your examination, I suggest that you have a glance through these proofs.

Practice questions C

(In these questions you are expected to prove any formulae that you may need for range, greatest height and time of flight,)

1 For the projectile illustrated below, the range is R m, the greatest height H m and the time of flight T seconds.

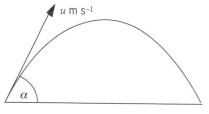

Prove that:

(a) $T^2 = \dfrac{8H}{g}$

(b) $H = \dfrac{R}{4}\tan\alpha$

(c) $R = \dfrac{T^2 g}{2}\cot\alpha$

2 An athlete throws the hammer with an initial speed of 24 m s^{-1} at an angle of 28° above the horizontal. At the instant of release the hammer is at a height of 1.4 m above the horizontal ground. By treating the hammer as a particle, and ignoring air resistance, show that the equation of the trajectory of the hammer is approximately

$$y = 1.4 + 0.53x - 0.01x^2,$$

where y metres is the height above the ground when the horizontal distance travelled by the hammer is x metres.

Hence calculate the horizontal distance between the point of release of the hammer and the point at which it hits the ground.

3 A particle is projected from point O with speed 9 m s^{-1}, in a direction which makes an angle of 70° with the horizontal. The horizontal and vertical displacements of the particle from O after t seconds are x metres and y metres respectively.

(a) Write down expressions for x and y in terms of t, and hence show that

$$y = 2.75x - 0.52x^2$$

is an approximation for the equation of the path of the particle.

(b) Find the range of the particle on the horizontal plane through O.

4 A projectile is fired, at time $t = 0$, from a point O on horizontal ground. The horizontal and vertical components of the initial velocity of the projectile are 30 m s^{-1} and 45 m s^{-1} respectively. At time t seconds, the projectile is at the point whose coordinates, in metres, are (x, y) referred to horizontal and vertically upward axes at O. Assuming that the motion may be modelled by that of a particle moving with constant acceleration, express x and y in terms of t and hence show that the equation of the trajectory is given approximately by

$$y = \dfrac{3x}{2} - \dfrac{49x^2}{9000}$$

The projectile hits the ground at A. Use the above equation to find the distance OA.

How to tackle problems involving variable acceleration   OCR M1 5.7.3 (c)

When the *acceleration varies we cannot use the four constant acceleration equations.* So what do we do?

We saw in Section 2 of Unit M1 that the gradient of the distance–time graph gave the velocity. If this distance–time graph was a curve, then we had to estimate this velocity by drawing in a tangent. And so we had:

Figure 1.10

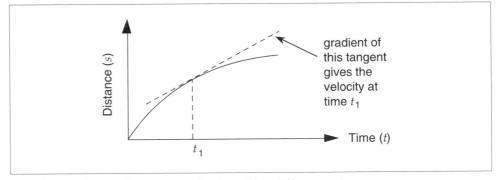

But the gradient of a curve can be found by differentiation:

$$\therefore \quad \text{Velocity} = \frac{ds}{dt} = v$$

We also saw in Section 2, that the gradient of the velocity–time graph gave the acceleration. And so we also had:

Figure 1.11

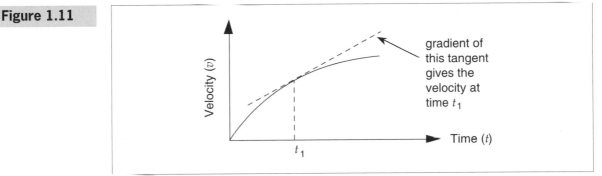

But the gradient of the above curve can also be found by differentiation.

$$\therefore \quad \text{Acceleration} = \frac{dv}{dt} = \frac{d^2s}{dt^2}$$

And so, if we want to go from the velocity formula to the acceleration formula, we just differentiate. If we want to do it the other way round, i.e. go from the acceleration formula to the velocity formula, then we integrate (but don't forget + c!). Let's summarise what we've got:

Differentiate $\downarrow$	Displacement $= s$ Velocity $= \dfrac{ds}{dt} = v$ Acceleration $= \dfrac{d^2s}{dt^2} = \dfrac{dv}{dt}$	$\uparrow$ Integrate (and don't forget $+c$)

Example	The velocity, v m s^{-1}, of a particle moving in a straight line t seconds after the beginning of the motion is given by $v = 2 + 4t + t^3$. Find the initial acceleration.

Solution	$v = 2 + 4t + t^3 \Rightarrow$ acceleration $= \dfrac{dv}{dt} = 4 + 3t^2$
	Initially $t = 0$ ∴ initial acceleration $= 4 + 0 = 4$ m s^{-2}.

Example	The distance s metres moved by a particle travelling in a straight line in t seconds is given by $s = 2t + t^3$. Calculate:
	(a) the average velocity over the first 3 seconds
	(b) the velocity after 3 seconds.

Solution	(a) $t = 3 \Rightarrow s = 2 \times 3 + 3^3 = 33$
	∴ Particle covers 33 m in 3 seconds
	∴ Average velocity $= 11$ m s^{-1}
	(b) $v = \dfrac{ds}{dt} = 2 + 3t^2$
	∴ $t = 3 \Rightarrow v = 2 + 3 \times 3^2 = 29$ ∴ Velocity $= 29$ m s^{-1}

Example	A point moves in a straight line so that its acceleration in m s^{-2} is given by $f = t^2 + 2t$, where t is the time in seconds. If the initial velocity is 4 m s^{-1}, find the velocity after 3 seconds.

Solution	Acceleration $= \dfrac{dv}{dt} = t^2 + 2t$
	Integrate and get $v = \dfrac{t^3}{3} + t^2 + c$
	But $v = 4$ when $t = 0$ ∴ $c = 4$
	∴ Velocity formula is $v = \dfrac{t^3}{3} + t^2 + 4$
	∴ $t = 3 \Rightarrow v = \dfrac{3^3}{3} + 3^2 + 4 = 22$
	∴ Velocity $= 22$ m s^{-1}
	In this question f was used for acceleration (rather than a). You need to be aware of both notations.

Example	A train runs non-stop between two stations P and Q, and its velocity, t hrs after leaving P, is $60t - 30t^2$ km/h. Find the distance between P and Q.

Solution	Stops when $v = 0 \Rightarrow 60t - 30t^2 = 0$
	$\Rightarrow 30t(2 - t) = 0$
	$\Rightarrow t = 0$ or 2
	∴ The train takes 2 hours travelling from P to Q.

But velocity $= \dfrac{ds}{dt} = 60t - 30t^2$

Integrate and get $s = 30t^2 - 10t^3 + c$

But $s = 0$ when $t = 0$ $\therefore$ $c = 0$

$\therefore$ Distance formula is $s = 30t^2 - 10t^3$

$\therefore$ $t = 2 \Rightarrow s = 30 \times 4 - 10 \times 8 = 40$

$\therefore$ Distance between P and $Q = 40$ km

Example

The position vector of a particle at time t seconds is given by:

$$\mathbf{r} = (8t^3\mathbf{i} + t^4\mathbf{j}) \text{ m}$$

Find its velocity and acceleration after 2 seconds.

Solution

We differentiate to get the velocity vector. We could use any of the symbols

$\mathbf{v}, \dfrac{d\mathbf{r}}{dt}$ or $\dot{\mathbf{r}}$ to represent this velocity vector but $\dot{\mathbf{r}}$ is the most common.

$\therefore$ Velocity vector $= \dot{\mathbf{r}} = 24t^2\mathbf{i} + 4t^3\mathbf{j}$

$\therefore$ $t = 2 \Rightarrow \dot{\mathbf{r}} = (96\mathbf{i} + 32\mathbf{j})$ m s^{-1}

Now differentiate again to get the acceleration vector (and $\ddot{\mathbf{r}}$ is the popular notation this time.)

$\therefore$ Acceleration vector $= \ddot{\mathbf{r}} = 48t\mathbf{i} + 12t^2\mathbf{j}$

$\therefore$ $t = 2 \Rightarrow \ddot{\mathbf{r}} = (96\mathbf{i} + 48\mathbf{j})$ m s^{-2}

Example

A particle has velocity vector $\mathbf{v}$, where $\mathbf{v} = (2t\mathbf{i} + 3t^2\mathbf{j})$ m s^{-1}, at time t seconds.

Initially the particle is at a point whose position vector is $(\mathbf{i} + 4\mathbf{j})$ m.

Find the position vector of the particle at time t.

Solution

We integrate to get the position vector.

$\therefore$ $\dot{\mathbf{r}} = 2t\mathbf{i} + 3t^2\mathbf{j} \Rightarrow \mathbf{r} = t^2\mathbf{i} + t^3\mathbf{j} + \mathbf{c}$

(Don't forget the $+ \mathbf{c}$ when integrating. In this case $\mathbf{c}$ is a constant *vector*.)

But when $t = 0$, $\mathbf{r} = \mathbf{i} + 4\mathbf{j}$ $\therefore$ $\mathbf{c} = \mathbf{i} + 4\mathbf{j}$

$\Rightarrow \mathbf{r} = t^2\mathbf{i} + t^3\mathbf{j} + \mathbf{i} + 4\mathbf{j}$

$\Rightarrow \mathbf{r} = (t^2 + 1)\mathbf{i} + (t^3 + 4)\mathbf{j}$, the required position vector.

Practice questions D

1 The displacement, x m, of a particle moving in a straight line t seconds after the beginning of the motion is given by $x = 5t^3 + 7t^2 + 2t$. Find the displacement, velocity and acceleration after 2 seconds.

2 A particle starting from rest at O moves along a straight line OA so that its acceleration after t seconds is $(6t + 5)$ m s^{-2}. Find the acceleration and velocity of the particle after 2 seconds.

3 A particle is moving along a straight line OA so that its acceleration, t seconds after passing through O, is given by $(12t-1)$ m s^{-2}. The velocity of the particle as it passed through O was 5 m s^{-1}. Find the acceleration and velocity of the particle after 2 seconds.

4 Referred to a fixed origin O, the position vector of a particle P at time t seconds is $\mathbf{r}$ metres where
$$\mathbf{r} = 5t^2\mathbf{i} + t^3\,\mathbf{j},\ t \geq 0$$
At the instant when $t = 2$, find:

(a) the velocity of P, giving your answer as a vector

(b) the speed of P

(c) the acceleration of P, giving your answer as a vector.

5 The acceleration $\mathbf{a}$ m s^{-2} of a particle P in m s^{-1} at a time t seconds is given as
$$\mathbf{a} = 12t\mathbf{i} + 3\mathbf{j}$$
When $t = 0$, the velocity of P is $(4\mathbf{i} + 2\mathbf{j})$ m s^{-1}.

(a) Find the velocity of P when $t = 2$.

When $t = 2$, the direction of motion of P makes an angle θ with the vector $\mathbf{j}$.

(b) Find, to the nearest degree, the value of θ.

6 With respect to a fixed origin O, the velocity $\mathbf{v}$ m s^{-1} of a particle at time t seconds is given by
$$\mathbf{v} = 2t^2\mathbf{i} + (6 - 3t)\mathbf{j}$$

(a) Find the acceleration of P at time t seconds, giving your answer as a vector.

(b) Find the value of t when P is moving parallel to the vector $\mathbf{i}$.

When $t = 0$, P is at the point with position vector $-2\mathbf{i}$.

(c) Find, to 3 significant figures, the distance OP when $t = 3$.

7 A particle P moves along the x-axis. It passes through the origin O at time $t = 0$ with speed 12 m s^{-1} in the direction of x increasing. At time t seconds the acceleration of P in the direction of x increasing is $(6t - 20)$ m s^{-2}.

(a) Find the values of t at which P is instantaneously at rest.

(b) Find the distance between the points at which P is instantaneously at rest.

8 A particle moves along the x-axis and passes through the origin O with speed 6 m s^{-1} in the positive x direction. At time t seconds after passing through O the acceleration of the particle is $(6t + 7)$ m s^{-2}.

(a) Find the speed of the particle when $t = 2$.

(b) Find the distance of the particle from O at time t seconds.

(c) Hence find the distance covered by the particle between the instants when $t = 3$ and $t = 5$.

9 A particle P of mass 1.2 kg moves under the action of a single force $\mathbf{F}$ newtons. At time t seconds, its position vector $\mathbf{r}$ metres relative to a fixed origin O is given by
$$\mathbf{r} = (3t^2 + 1)\mathbf{i} + (2t - 6t^2)\mathbf{j}$$
where $\mathbf{i}$ and $\mathbf{j}$ are perpendicular unit vectors. Show that $\mathbf{F}$ is a constant and find its magnitude.

10 A particle P is initially at the origin O, which is fixed. At time $t = 0$, P is projected from O and moves so that, at time t seconds, its position vector $\mathbf{r}$ metres relative to O is given by
$$\mathbf{r} = (t^3 + 2t)\mathbf{i} + (5t^2 - 5t)\mathbf{j},\ t \geq 0$$

(a) Find the velocity vector of P at time t seconds.

(b) Hence find the times at which P is moving in a direction parallel to the vector $\mathbf{i} + \mathbf{j}$.

11 A particle P moves in a straight line in such a way that, at time t seconds, its velocity v m s^{-1} is given by
$$v = \begin{cases} 4t - 3t^2, & 0 \leq t \leq 4 \\ -512t^{-2}, & t > 4 \end{cases}$$
When $t = 0$, P is at O.

Calculate the displacement of P from O

(a) when $t = 4$

(b) when $t = 5$.

12 The displacement, x m, of a particle moving in a straight line t seconds after the beginning of the motion is given by
$$x = 3e^t + t + 1$$
Find the velocity and acceleration at time t.

13 A particle P moves in a straight line in such a way that, at time t seconds, its velocity v m s^{-1} is given by

$$v = \begin{cases} 2e^t + 2t, & 0 \le t \le 2 \\ e^2t + 8t^{-1}, & t > 2 \end{cases}$$

When $t = 0$, P is at O. Calculate the displacement of P from O

(a) when $t = 2$

(b) when $t = 3$.

SUMMARY EXERCISE

1 A stone falls past a window 3 m high in 0.8 seconds. Find the height from which the stone fell.

2 A ball is thrown vertically upwards with a speed of 40 m s^{-1}. If it falls past the point of projection into a well of depth 75 m, find when it strikes the bottom.

3 A block falls from a mast-head, and is observed to take 0.5 seconds in falling from the deck to the bottom of the hold, a distance of 8 m. Calculate the height of the mast-head above the deck.

4

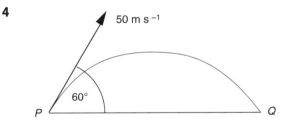

An object is projected from P with velocity 50 m s^{-1} inclined at 60° to the horizontal PQ. Find:

(a) the time of flight

(b) the range PQ

(c) the greatest height above PQ

(d) the height above PQ after 2 seconds

(e) the direction of flight after 3 seconds.

5 OP is a cliff 100 m high.

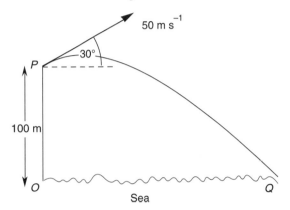

A ball is projected from P with velocity 50 m s^{-1} at 30° to the horizontal. Find:

(a) the greatest height of the ball above the sea

(b) the time taken to hit the sea

(c) the range OQ

(d) the velocity at Q, in magnitude and direction.

6 OP is a cliff 100 m high.

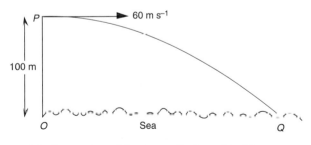

A ball is projected horizontally from P with velocity 60 m s^{-1}. Find:

(a) the time taken to hit the sea

(b) the range OQ

(c) the height above the sea after 2 seconds

(d) the direction of flight after 3 seconds

(e) the velocity after 3 seconds.

7

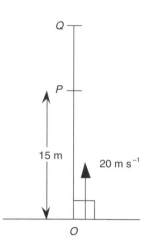

A ball is projected vertically upwards with velocity 20 m s⁻¹. It just reaches Q and then falls back down again. Find:

(a)   the time taken to reach P (where $OP = 15$ m)

(b)   the time from P to Q

(c)   the distance from P to Q

(d)   the time the ball is above P.

8   A jet of water leaves a hose-pipe with horizontal and vertical velocities of 15 m s⁻¹ and 25 m s⁻¹. Find for how long each particle of water is in the air, and how far the jet reaches.

9   A particle P is projected with speed u m s⁻¹ at an angle of elevation θ where $\sin\theta = \frac{12}{13}$

from a point A on a horizontal plane. The particle moves freely under gravity and strikes the horizontal plane at the point B, where $AB = 600$ m.

(a)   Show that $u = 91$.

(b)   Calculate the greatest height reached by P above the horizontal plane.

(c)   Calculate the time taken for P to reach B from A.

10   Find the range of a shell fired with muzzle velocity of 700 m s⁻¹ at 15° to the horizontal.

11   The distance x at time t is given by $x = 4t^3 + 8t + 2$.

Find the velocity and acceleration when $t = 2$.

12   The distance x at time t is given by
$x = 2t(t + 1)(t + 2)$.

Find the velocity and acceleration when $t = 2$.

13   The distance x at time t is given by $x = t^2 + t + 7$, when x is measured in metres and t in seconds. What is the velocity after 3 seconds? When does the velocity equal 9 m s⁻¹?

14   The acceleration of a particle is given by $f = 12t^2$, where f has units m s⁻² and t is measured in seconds. After 1 second the velocity is 6 m s⁻¹. Find the velocity as a function of t. What is the initial velocity and when does the velocity equal 500 m s⁻¹?

15   The velocity of a particle in m s⁻¹ is given by $v = 3t^2 - \frac{1}{3}t^3 + 9$, where t is measured in seconds.

When does the acceleration equal zero? What is the distance covered between these two times?

16   A stopping train travels between two adjacent stations so that its velocity is v km/min, t minutes after leaving the first, where $v = \frac{4t}{3}(1 - t)$. Find:

(a)   the average velocity for the journey in km/h

(b)   the maximum velocity in km/h.

17   The formula connecting the velocity and time for the motion of a particle is $v = 1 + 4t + 6t^2$. Find the average velocity and the average acceleration for the interval $t = 1$ to $t = 3$, the units being metres and seconds.

18   A racing car starts from rest and its acceleration after t seconds is $(k - \frac{1}{6}t)$ m s⁻² until it reaches a velocity of 60 m s⁻¹ at the end of 1 minute. Find the value of k, and the distance travelled in the first minute.

19   A particle starting from rest at O moves along a straight line OA so that its acceleration after t seconds is $(24t - 12t^2)$ m s⁻².

(a)   Find when it again returns to O and its velocity, then,

(b)   find its maximum displacement from O during this interval,

(c)   what is its maximum velocity and its greatest speed during this interval?

20 P and R are two adjacent railway stations, and Q is a signal box on the line between them. A train which stops at P and R has a velocity $(\frac{3}{8} + \frac{1}{2}t - \frac{1}{2}t^2)$ km/min at t minutes past noon, and it passes Q at noon. Find:

(a)   the times of departure from P and arrival at R

(b)   an expression for the distance of the train from P in terms of t

(c)   the average velocity between P and R, in km h⁻¹

(d)   the maximum velocity attained, in km h⁻¹.

21 A stone thrown upwards from the top of a vertical cliff 56 m high falls into the sea 4 seconds later, 32 m from the foot of the cliff. Find the speed and direction of projection. (The stone moves in a vertical plane perpendicular to the cliff.)

22 A tile slides down a roof inclined at 30° to the horizontal starting 5 m from the edge of the roof. Assuming the roof is smooth find the horizontal distance from the edge of the roof that the tile hits the ground, if the edge of the roof is 8 m above the ground level.

23 A particle starts from rest at time $t = 0$ and moves in a straight line with variable acceleration f m/s², where

$$f = \frac{t}{5} \text{ for } 0 \le t < 5$$

$$f = \frac{t}{5} + \frac{10}{t^2} \text{ for } t \ge 5$$

t being measured in seconds. Show that the velocity is 2.5 m/s when $t = 5$ and 11 m/s when $t = 10$.

24 A particle moves in a straight line with a velocity of v m/s after t seconds, where $v = 3t^2 + 2t$. Find:

(a) the acceleration at the end of 2 seconds

(b) the distance it travels in the 4th second.

25 A particle P moves from rest, at a point O at time $t = 0$ seconds, along a straight line. At any subsequent time t seconds, the acceleration of P is proportional to $(7 - t^2)$ m/s² and the displacement of P from O is s metres. The speed of P is 6 m/s when $t = 3$.

(a) Show that $s = \frac{1}{24} t^2 (42 - t^2)$

(b) Find the total distance, in metres, that P moves before returning to O.

26 A golf ball is projected with speed 49 m/s at an angle of elevation α from a point A on the first floor of a golf driving range. Point A is at a height of $3\frac{4}{15}$ metres above horizontal ground. The ball first strikes the ground at a point Q which is at a horizontal distance of 98 m from the point A as shown in the following diagram.

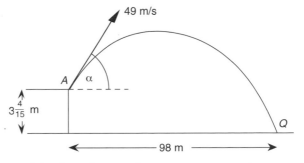

(a) Show that $6 \tan^2 \alpha - 30 \tan \alpha + 5 = 0$.*

(b) Hence find, to the nearest degree, the two possible angles of elevation.

(c) Find, to the nearest second, the smallest possible time of direct flight from A to Q. [*Hint: You will need to use the identities $\frac{\sin \alpha}{\cos \alpha} = \tan \alpha$ (which you met in Unit P1) and $\frac{1}{\cos^2 \alpha} = 1 + \tan^2 \alpha$ (which you met in Unit P2)

27 The position vector **r** cm of a particle at time t seconds is given by

$$\mathbf{r} = 3(t - 1)\mathbf{i} + 4(3 - t)\mathbf{j}$$

(a) Using graph paper, draw the path of the particle for $0 \le t \le 4$.

(b) For what value of t is the particle closest to the origin?

(c) Using (b), calculate the least distance of the particle from the origin.

28 A particle P moves so that, at time t seconds, its position vector, **r** m, relative to a fixed origin, is given by $\mathbf{r} = (t^2 - 4t)\mathbf{i} + (t^3 + ft^2)\mathbf{j}$, $t > 0$, where f is a constant.

(a) Find an expression for the velocity of P at time t.

(b) Given that the particle comes to instantaneous rest, find the value of f.

29 A particle P moves so that at time t seconds its position vector **r** metres, relative to a final origin O, is given by:

$$\mathbf{r} = (2t - 3t^2 - 1)\mathbf{i} + (2t^2 - 2)\mathbf{j}$$

(a) Find the velocity of P when $t = 2$

(b) Hence find the speed of P when $t = 2$.

SUMMARY

In this section we have:

- used the following models when tackling projectile questions:
  - bodies are assumed to be particles
  - the acceleration due to gravity is assumed to be a constant 9.8 m s^{-2}.
  - there is no air resistance.

- used the following tricks in projectile questions:
  - time to go up equals time to come back down
  - initial speed going up equals the final speed coming down.

- used the following layout when takling projectile questions:

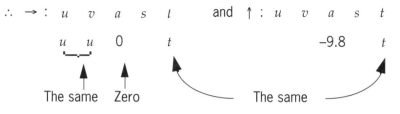

- worked out the direction of flight, by working out the horizontal and vertical components of velocity

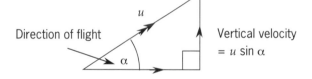

Direction of flight

Vertical velocity = $u \sin \alpha$

Horizontal velocity = $u \cos \alpha$

- tackled variable acceleration problems by means of the following table:

Differentiate	Displacement = s	Integrate (and don't forget + c)
	Velocity = $\dfrac{ds}{dt}$ = v	
	Acceleration = $\dfrac{d^2s}{dt^2}$ = $\dfrac{dv}{dt}$	

- found the *initial* velocity (find v when $t = 0$)

- found the *maximum* velocity (put acceleration = 0, find t and hence v)

- found the *average* velocity (divide the total displacement by the total time)

- found the *average* acceleration (divide the increase in velocity by the total time).

ANSWERS

Practice questions A

1 0.639 sec (3 s.f.)
2 276 m (3 s.f.)
3 2.04 sec (3 s.f.)
4 1.38 sec (3 s.f.)
5 2.86 sec (3 s.f.)
6 (a) 2.5 m
   (b) 0.714 sec (3 s.f.)
   (c) 1.43 sec (3 s.f.)
7 3 sec
8 370 m (3 s.f) above the ground
9 4.9 m
10 6.46 sec (3 s.f.)
11 6.12 seconds, 43.0 m (3 s.f.)

Practice questions B

[Non exact answers are given correct to 3 s.f.]
1 4.04 sec, 60.6 m
2 19.2 m, 0.639 sec
3 990 m s^{-1}
4 1.88 m
5 Fails. Ball lands 7.84 m from the boundary
6 14.8 m
7 10.1 m s^{-1}, 26.3 m s^{-1} at 67.4° to the horizontal
8 (a) 2.47 sec
   (b) 40.4 m
9 (a) Falling $PQ = 1.30$ m
   (b) 8.08
10 39.2°, 27.1 m s^{-1}
11 25.6 m s^{-1} at 73.5° with the downward vertical
12 (a) 46.3, 57.3°
   (b) 77.6

Practice questions C

2 55.5 m
3 (a) $x = 9 \cos 70° \times t$, $y = 90 \sin 70° \times t - 4.9t^2$
   (b) 5.29 m
4 $x = 30t$, $y = 45t - 4.9t^2$, $275\frac{25}{49}$ m

Practice questions D

1 72 m, 90 m s^{-1}, 74 m s^{-2}
2 17 m s^{-2}, 22 m s^{-1}
3 23 m s^{-2}, 27 m s^{-1}
4 (a) $(20\mathbf{i} + 12\mathbf{j})$ m s^{-1}
   (b) $\sqrt{544} \sim 23.3$ m s^{-1}
   (c) $(10\mathbf{i} + 12\mathbf{j})$ m s^{-2}
5 (a) $(28\mathbf{i} + 8\mathbf{j})$ m s^{-1} (b) 74.1°
6 (a) $(4t\mathbf{i} - 3\mathbf{j})$ m s^{-2}
   (b) 2   (c) $\sqrt{276.25} \sim 16.6$ m
7 (a) $\frac{2}{3}$ or 6   (b) $75\frac{23}{27}$
8 (a) 32 m s^{-1} (b) $t^3 + 3.5\,t^2 + 6t$
   (c) 166 m
9 $\mathbf{F} = 7.2\mathbf{i} - 14.4\mathbf{j}$ $\therefore$ magnitude $= 16.1$ N (3 s.f.)
10 (a) $\left((3t^2 + 2)\mathbf{i} + (10t - 5)\mathbf{j}\right)$ m s^{-1}
    (b) 1 sec or $2\frac{1}{3}$ seconds
11 (a) -32 m   (b) -57.6 m
12 $x = 3e^t + 1$ and $\dot{x} = 3e^t$
13 (a) $(2e^2 + 2)$ m ~ 16.8 m
    (b) $(4.5e^2 + 8 \ln 1.5 + 2)$ m ~ 38.5 m

2
Centres of mass

| INTRODUCTION | If I gave you a saucer and asked you to balance it on your finger, you would do this by putting your finger under the centre of the saucer. |

This centre is called the *centre of mass* of the saucer.

However, if you now put a biscuit over one end, where would you have to put your finger now in order to balance it?

It would certainly be a point away from the centre of the saucer and nearer the biscuit. Once the point has been found, that point would be the centre of mass of the saucer and biscuit.

In this section we'll see how to set about finding balancing points for objects such as these.

When you have finished this section you should be able to:

● find the position of the centre of mass of one and two dimensional shapes

● work out angles when bodies are suspended in equilibrium.

Centre of mass of one-dimensional shapes

OCR M2 5.8.1 (b),(d)

The centre of mass of any shape is the point about which it balances.

Suppose we are given a light rod *AB* of length 9 m with masses of 4 kg, 5 kg and 6 kg attached as shown.

Figure 2.1	

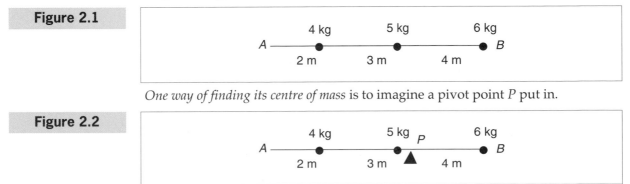

One way of finding its centre of mass is to imagine a pivot point P put in.

Figure 2.2	

21

Now put in all the forces.

Figure 2.3

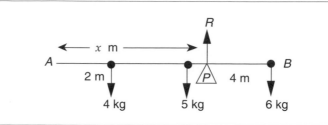

Resolving vertically we get $R = 15$ kg ...①

Then $A \curvearrowright$: 4 kg $\times 2 + 5$ kg $\times 5 + 6$ kg $\times 9 = 15$ kg $\times x$ (Using ①)

$\Rightarrow 4 \times 2 + 5 \times 5 + 6 \times 9 = 15 \times x$ ...(*)

$\Rightarrow x = 5.8$ m

∴ centre of mass of the system is 5.8 m from A.

A better way of finding its centre of mass is to go straight to equation(*)!

Set up a table of masses and distances (from point A).

	Separate masses			Total mass
Masses (kg)	4	5	6	15
Distance from A (m)	2	5	9	$\bar{x}$

Then just multiply as you go along.

∴ $4 \times 2 + 5 \times 5 + 6 \times 9 = 15\bar{x}$

∴ $\bar{x} = 5.8$ m, as before.

(It is conventional to use $\bar{x}$ rather than x when finding a centre of mass.)

Example

Find the centre of mass of the following system of particles.

Figure 2.4

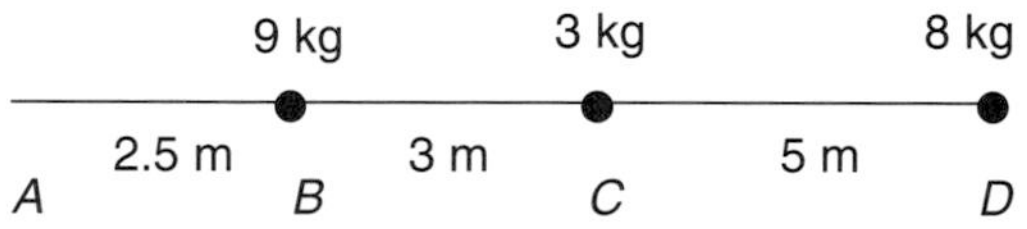

9 kg   3 kg   8 kg

2.5 m   3 m   5 m

A B C D

Solution

	B +	C +	D =	Whole thing
Masses (kg)	9	3	8	20
Distance from A (m)	2.5	5.5	10.5	$\bar{x}$

∴ $9 \times 2.5 + 3 \times 5.5 + 8 \times 10.5 = 20\bar{x}$

∴ $\bar{x} = 6.15$

∴   Centre of mass is 6.15 m from A.

Example	A cylindrical can is made of a metal of uniform density. The base radius is 3 cm and the height is 8 cm. It has a base but no lid.

Figure 2.5

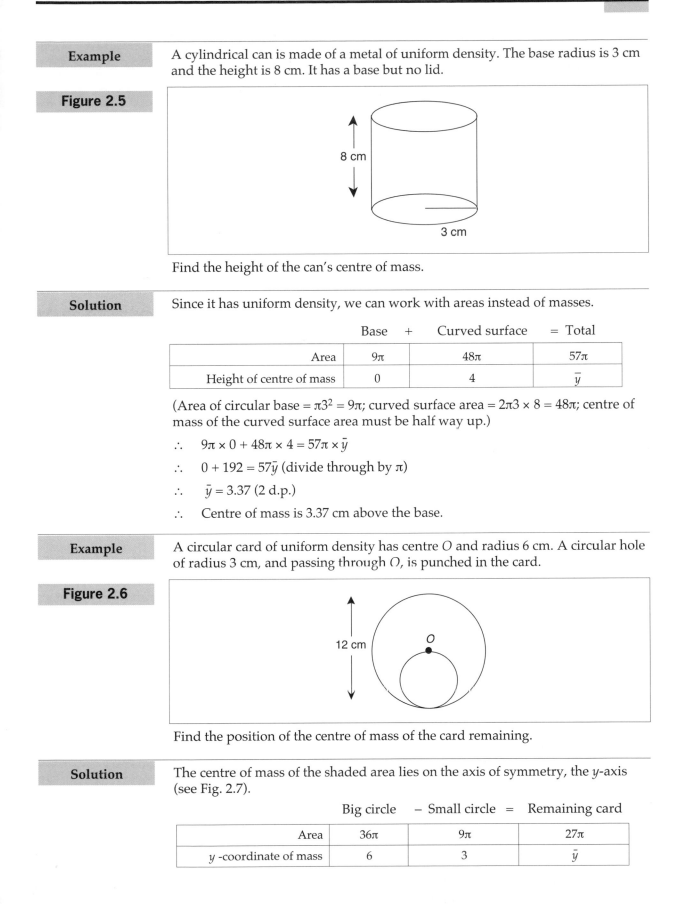

Find the height of the can's centre of mass.

Solution	Since it has uniform density, we can work with areas instead of masses.

	Base	+	Curved surface	= Total
Area	9π		48π	57π
Height of centre of mass	0		4	$\bar{y}$

(Area of circular base = $\pi3^2 = 9\pi$; curved surface area = $2\pi3 \times 8 = 48\pi$; centre of mass of the curved surface area must be half way up.)

∴ $9\pi \times 0 + 48\pi \times 4 = 57\pi \times \bar{y}$

∴ $0 + 192 = 57\bar{y}$ (divide through by π)

∴ $\bar{y} = 3.37$ (2 d.p.)

∴   Centre of mass is 3.37 cm above the base.

Example	A circular card of uniform density has centre O and radius 6 cm. A circular hole of radius 3 cm, and passing through O, is punched in the card.

Figure 2.6

Find the position of the centre of mass of the card remaining.

Solution	The centre of mass of the shaded area lies on the axis of symmetry, the y-axis (see Fig. 2.7).

	Big circle	– Small circle	= Remaining card
Area	36π	9π	27π
y -coordinate of mass	6	3	$\bar{y}$

Figure 2.7

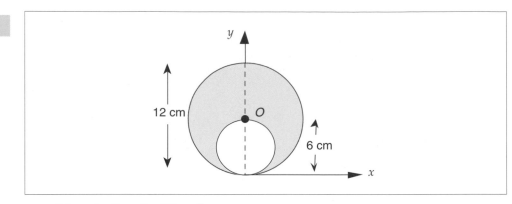

$\therefore \quad 36\pi \times 6 - 9\pi \times 3 = 27\pi \times \bar{y}$

$\therefore \quad 216 - 27 = 27\bar{y} \therefore \bar{y} = 7$

$\therefore$ Card has centre of mass 7 cm up the axis of symmetry.

Practice questions A

1 Consider the following system of particles:

2 kg 3 kg 5 kg

A 1 m B 2 m C 3 m D

Find the distance of the centre of the mass from A.

2 Consider the following system of particles:

6 kg 3 kg 5 kg 6 kg

A 1 m B 2 m C 2 m D

Find the distance at the centre of mass from A.

3 Consider the following system of particles:

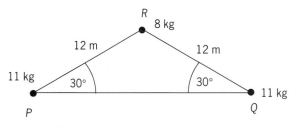

Find the distance of the centre of mass from PQ.

4 A cylindrical can is made of a metal of uniform density. The base radius is 5 cm and the height is 8 cm. It has a base but no lid.

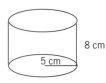

Find the height of the can's centre of mass.

5 Consider the following system of particles:

2 kg 5 kg x kg

A 1 m B 3m C 2m D

The centre of mass of the system is 5 m from A. Find the value of x.

6 Consider the following system of particles:

3 kg 4 kg x kg

A 2 m B 5 m C

The centre of mass of the system is 4 m from A. Find the value of x.

7 A uniform rod AC of mass 8 kg and length 10 m has masses attached as shown:

2 kg 3 kg x kg

A 2 m B 8 m C

The centre of mass of the system is 4 m from A. Find the value of x.

8 Consider the following system of particles:

x kg 2x kg 8 kg

A 3 m B 6 m C

The centre of mass of the system is 4 m from A. Find the value of x.

9 Two similar uniform rods each 6 m in length and weighing respectively 20 kg and 30 kg are joined end to end in a straight line. Find the distance of the centre of mass of the combined rod from the junction.

10 A cylindrical can has diameter 4 m and height 3 m. The flat base and curved walls are made of thin tin weighing 1 kg per m², the flat top is made of thin tin weighing 0.5 kg per m². Find the height of the centre of mass of the tin above the base.

Centre of mass of two-dimensional shapes

OCR M2 5.8.1 (b),(d)

With two-dimensional shapes *without an axis of symmetry*, you need two rows of distances, i.e. two axes. Otherwise it's the same as before.

Example

A 4 × 4 piece of card of uniform density has a 2 × 2 square removed from the top right-hand corner.

Figure 2.8

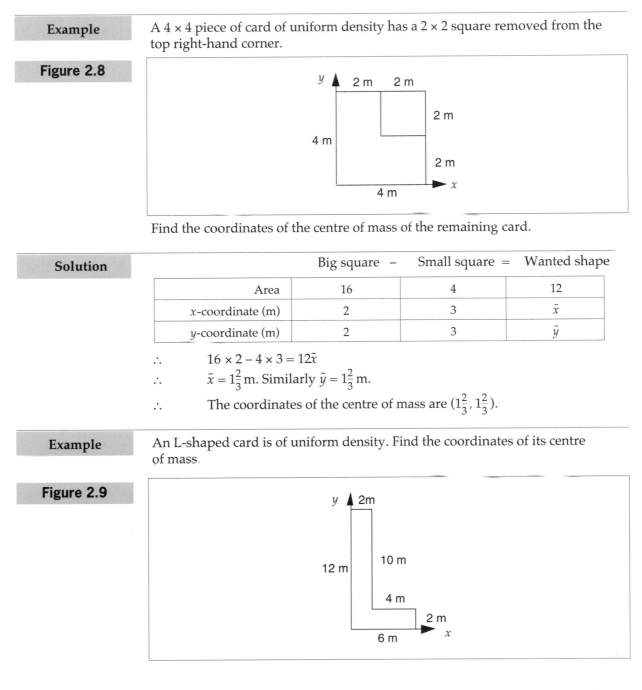

Find the coordinates of the centre of mass of the remaining card.

Solution

	Big square	− Small square	= Wanted shape
Area	16	4	12
x-coordinate (m)	2	3	$\bar{x}$
y-coordinate (m)	2	3	$\bar{y}$

∴ $16 \times 2 - 4 \times 3 = 12\bar{x}$

∴ $\bar{x} = 1\frac{2}{3}$ m. Similarly $\bar{y} = 1\frac{2}{3}$ m.

∴ The coordinates of the centre of mass are $(1\frac{2}{3}, 1\frac{2}{3})$.

Example

An L-shaped card is of uniform density. Find the coordinates of its centre of mass.

Figure 2.9

Solution	Separate into two areas A and B as shown.
Figure 2.10	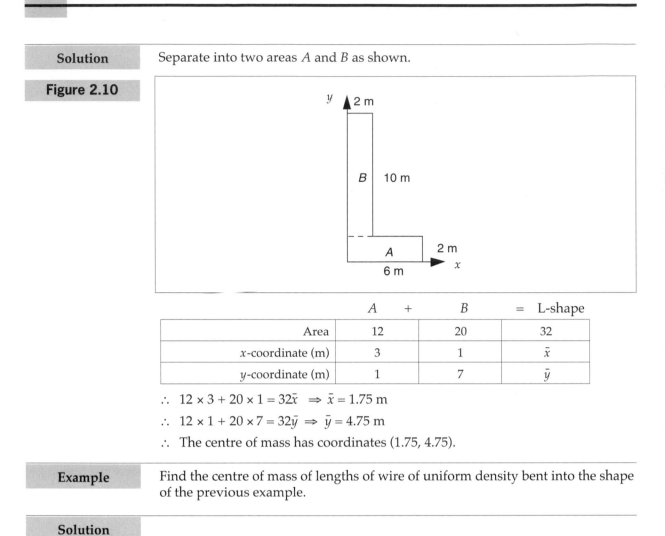

	A	$+$	B	$=$	L-shape
Area	12		20		32
x-coordinate (m)	3		1		$\bar{x}$
y-coordinate (m)	1		7		$\bar{y}$

$\therefore \quad 12 \times 3 + 20 \times 1 = 32\bar{x} \ \Rightarrow \ \bar{x} = 1.75$ m

$\therefore \quad 12 \times 1 + 20 \times 7 = 32\bar{y} \ \Rightarrow \ \bar{y} = 4.75$ m

$\therefore$ The centre of mass has coordinates (1.75, 4.75).

Example	Find the centre of mass of lengths of wire of uniform density bent into the shape of the previous example.

Solution	
Figure 2.11	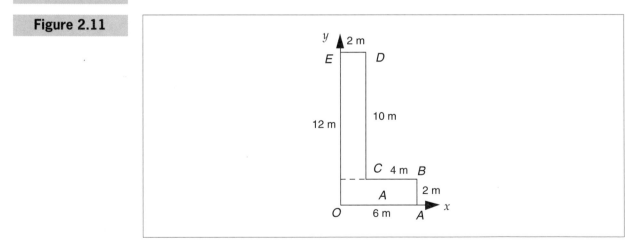

Since the wire is of uniform length, we work with lengths rather than masses.

	OA +	AB +	BC +	CD +	DE +	EO =	Whole thing
Length	6	2	4	10	2	12	36
x-coordinate (m)	3	6	4	2	1	0	$\bar{x}$
y-coordinate (m)	0	1	2	7	12	6	$\bar{y}$

$$\therefore\ 6 \times 3 + 2 \times 6 + 4 \times 4 + 10 \times 2 + 2 \times 1 + 12 \times 0 = 36\bar{x} \qquad \therefore\ \bar{x} = 1\tfrac{8}{9}\ \text{m}$$

$$\therefore\ 6 \times 0 + 2 \times 1 + 4 \times 2 + 10 \times 7 + 2 \times 12 + 12 \times 6 = 36\bar{y} \qquad \therefore\ \bar{y} = 4\tfrac{8}{9}\ \text{m}$$

$\therefore$ The centre of mass has coordinates $(1\tfrac{8}{9}, 4\tfrac{8}{9})$.

Practice questions B

1 The diagram shows a 6 × 8 piece of card *OABC* of uniform density with a 2 × 2 square removed from the top right-hand corner.

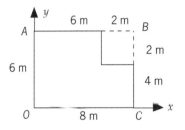

Find the coordinates of the centre of mass of the remaining card.

2 Find the centre of mass of a length of wire of uniform density bent into the shape of question 1 above.

3 The diagram shows an L-shaped card of uniform density.

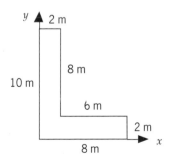

Find the coordinates of the centre of mass.

4 Find the centre of mass of a length of wire of uniform density bent into the shape of question 3 above.

5 Find the coordinates of the centre of mass of the lamina illustrated at the top of the next column:

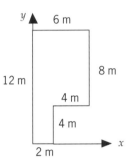

6 Find the coordinates of the centre of mass of a length of wire of uniform density bent into the shape of question 5 above.

7 A rectangle 3 m by 4 m is cut out from one corner of a square of side 6 m. Find the distance of the centre of mass of the remainder from the other two sides of the square.

8 *ABC* is a uniform rod of length 60 cm where *ABC* is a right angle and *AB = BC*. Find the position of the centre of mass.

9 *ABCD* is a square uniform sheet of thin metal of side 12 cm. A circle of radius 3 cm, the centre of which is 5 cm from *AB* and 4 cm from *BC*, is cut out and removed. Find the distance from *AB* and *BC* of the centre of mass of the remainder.

10 Consider the following system of particles:

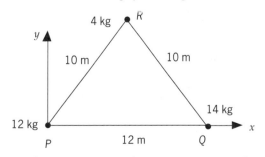

Find the coordinates of the centre of mass of the particles.

Some standard results

Some standard results, not obvious by symmetry, may be assumed in your examination. You wouldn't be expected to prove them but you might be asked to use them. These results are (for uniform bodies in each case):

Triangular lamina

Centre of mass, G, is a third of the way along a median from a side.

i.e. $MG = \frac{1}{3}MP$

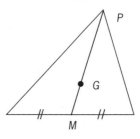

Solid pyramid

Centre of mass, G, is a quarter of the way up the height

i.e. $OG = \frac{1}{4}OP$

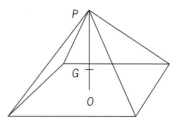

Solid cone

Centre of mass, G, is a quarter of the way up the height

i.e. $OG = \frac{1}{4}OP$

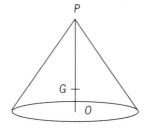

Solid hemisphere

Centre of mass, G, is three eighths of the way up the height

i.e. $OG = \frac{3}{8}OP$

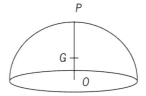

Semi-circular lamina

Centre of mass, G, is given by

i.e. $OG = \frac{4OP}{3\pi}$

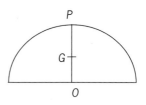

Should you be required to use these results, then they would be given to you in the question. There is no need to learn them by heart.

| Example | Find the position of the centre of mass, G, of the triangular lamina shown in Fig. 2.12. |

Figure 2.12

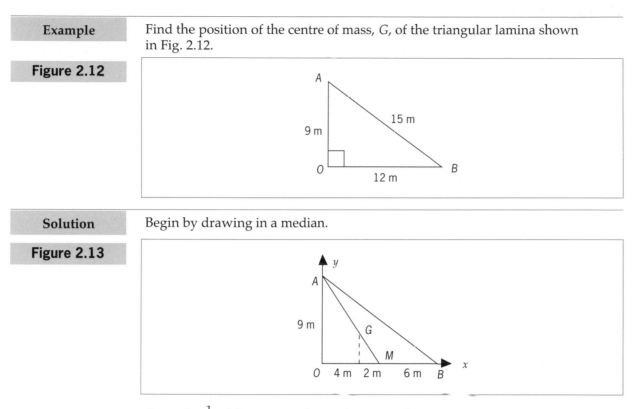

| Solution | Begin by drawing in a median. |

Figure 2.13

Since G is $\frac{1}{3}$ of the way up the median AM, the y-coordinate of G must be $\frac{1}{3} \times 9 = 3$ m. Similarly, the x-coordinate of G will be $\frac{1}{3}$ of the way back from M i.e. $\frac{1}{3} \times 6 = 2$ m back. Therefore the x-coordinate of G will be $6 - 2 = 4$ m.
$\therefore$ G has coordinates $(4, 3)$.

Practice questions C

1 Find the position of the centre of mass of the triangular lamina shown below;

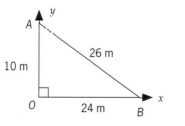

2 Find the height of the centre of mass of the triangular lamina shown below:

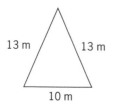

3 A solid cone has base radius 6 m and height 12 m. Find the height of the centre of mass above the base.

4 A solid hemisphere has radius 12 cm. Find the height of the centre of mass above the base.

5 A semi-circular lamina has radius 7 cm. Find the height of the centre of mass above the base.

6 Find the position of the centre of mass of the lamina shown below:

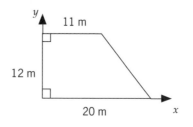

7 The lamina shown below consists of a rectangle and a semi-circle.

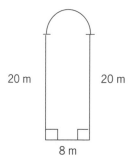

20 m   20 m

8 m

Find the height of the centre of mass of the lamina above the base.

8 A solid hemisphere radius 12 cm is glued centrally to one face of a solid cube (made of the same material) of side 24 cm. Find the position of the centre of mass of the combined solid from the common face.

9 A solid circular cone of height 12 cm and base radius 6 cm is joined to a circular cylinder of the same radius and length 20 cm so that they have the same central axis. Both solids are made of the same material. Find the distance of the centre of mass of the combined solid from the common base.

10 From a square uniform lamina *ABCD* of side 20 m a portion *CDE* in the form of an equilateral triangle is cut. Find the distance of the centre of mass from *AB*.

Bodies hanging in equilibrium

OCR **M2** 5.8.1 (a)

In an earlier example (see Fig. 2.8) we found the position of the centre of mass *G* of a 4 × 4 card with a 2 × 2 square removed from it. Our results were:

Figure 2.14

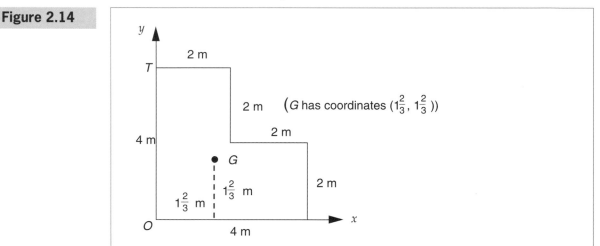

If this card is now suspended from the corner *T*, and allowed to hang freely, then *G* will swing round until it becomes vertically below *T*.

We will then have the set-up shown in Fig. 2.15.

∴ The angle that the edge *TO* makes with the downward vertical is given by:

$$\tan \theta = \frac{1\frac{2}{3}}{2\frac{1}{3}} \Rightarrow \theta = 35\frac{1}{2}^{\circ}$$

∴ In equilibrium, the edge *TO* makes an angle of $35\frac{1}{2}^{\circ}$ with the downward vertical.

Figure 2.15

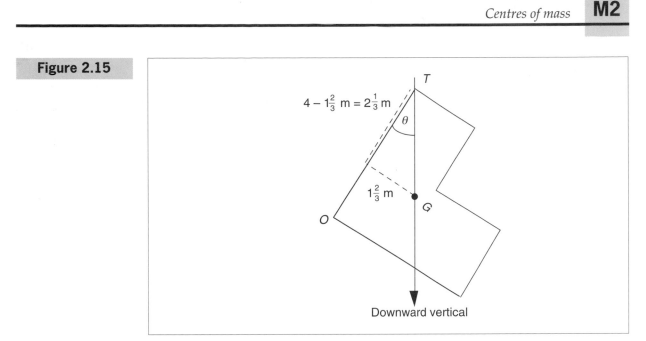

Easy enough, you may say, but the drawing of the second diagram could be tricky. The way you overcome this problem is to *take the first diagram, join T to G, and say that TG then represents the downward vertical*. And so:

Figure 2.16

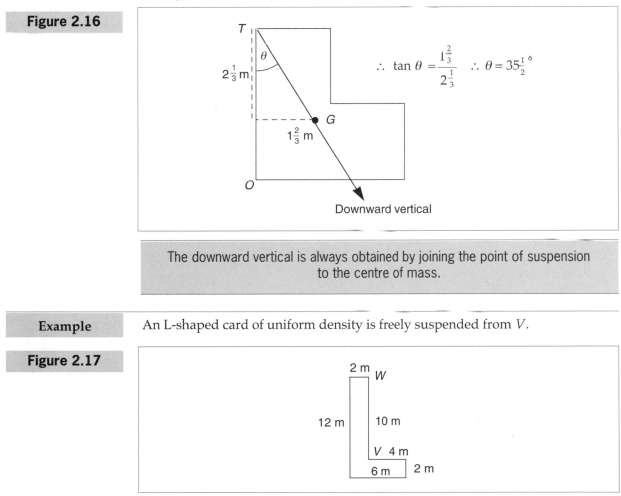

$$\therefore\ \tan \theta = \frac{1\frac{2}{3}}{2\frac{1}{3}}\ \ \therefore\ \theta = 35\frac{1}{2}°$$

> The downward vertical is always obtained by joining the point of suspension to the centre of mass.

Example   An L-shaped card of uniform density is freely suspended from *V*.

Figure 2.17

What angle does *VW* make with the downward vertical?

An earlier example (see Fig. 2.10) gave us the position of the centre of mass and so we have:

Figure 2.18

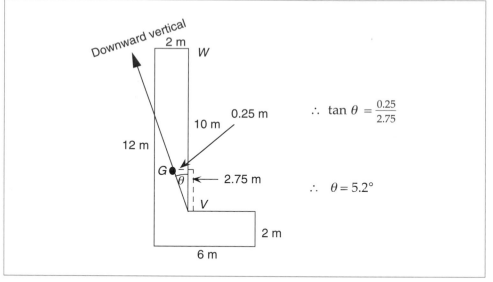

$$\therefore \quad \tan\theta = \frac{0.25}{2.75}$$

$$\therefore \quad \theta = 5.2°$$

$\therefore$ *VW* makes an angle of 5.2° with the downward vertical.

Practice questions D

1 A uniform square lamina *ABCD* is freely suspended from the point *P* on *AB*, where $AP = \frac{1}{3} AB$. The lamina hangs in equilibrium. Find the angle between *AB* and the vertical.

2 A thin *uniform wire of length 24 cm* is bent to form a framework in the shape of a right-angled triangle *PQR* where *PQ* = 6 cm, *QR* = 8 cm and *RP* = 10 cm. Find the distance of the centre of mass of the framework from:

(a) *PQ*   (b) *QR*.

The framework is freely suspended from the point *P* and hangs in equilibrium

(c) Find, to the nearest degree, the acute angle that *PQ* makes with the vertical.

3 A uniform triangular lamina *ABC* is in equilibrium, suspended from a fixed point *O* by a light inelastic string attached to the point *B* of the lamina, as shown below.

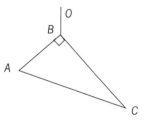

AB = 9 cm, *BC* = 12 cm and angle *ABC* = 90°. Calculate the angle of θ between *BC* and the downward vertical.

4 A uniform rectangular metal plate *ABCD*, where *AB* = 8 cm and *BC* = 3 cm, has mass *M*. Four particles of mass *m*, *m*, 4*m* and 4*m* are attached to the points *A*,*B*,*C* and *D* respectively. When the loaded plate is suspended freely from the point *A* and hangs in equilibrium, *AB* makes an angle θ with the downward vertical, as shown below, where $\tan\theta = 0.5$.

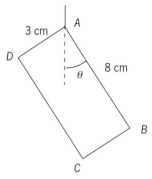

(a) Write down the distance of the centre of mass of the loaded plate from *AD*.

(b) Find the distance of the centre of mass of the loaded plate from *AB*.

(c) Hence find *m* in terms of *M*.

5 A *uniform rod of length 12 cm* is cut into three pieces, which are then joined to form the triangular frame shown below:

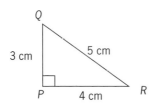

Find the distance of the centre of mass of the frame from

(a) *PQ*

(b) *PR*

The frame is then placed on a rough plane inclined at angle θ to the horizontal (as shown below):

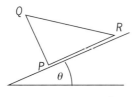

The plane is sufficiently rough to prevent slipping.

(c) If the framework is about to topple about *P*, find the angle θ, giving your answer correct to the nearest degree.

6 The diagram below shows a uniform lamina *ABCDE* consisting of a semi-circle *ADE* joined to a rectangle *ABCD*.

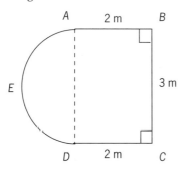

(a) Find the distance of the centre of mass of the lamina from *BC*

The lamina is freely suspended from the point *A* and hangs at rest.

(b) Find, to the nearest degree, the angle between *AD* and the vertical.

7 Consider the lamina below:

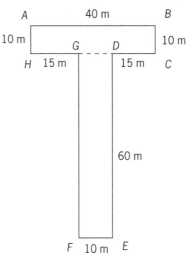

(a) Find the distance of the centre of mass of the lamina from *FE*. The lamina is freely suspended from *A* and hangs at rest.

(b) Find, to the nearest degree, the angle between *AB* and the vertical.

8 The lamina of question 1, Practice questions C, is freely suspended from point *A* and hangs at rest. Find, to the nearest degree, the angle between *AO* and the vertical.

9 The diagram below shows a semi-circular lamina of radius 6 cm hanging freely at rest.

Find the angle, θ, that *AB* makes with the downward vertical.

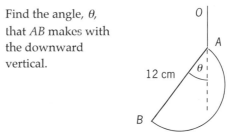

10 The diagram below shows a uniform solid hemisphere of radius 8 cm hanging freely at rest.

Find the angle, θ, that *AB* makes with the downward vertical.

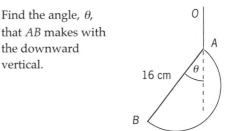

SUMMARY EXERCISE

1

A uniformly heavy rod *AB* is of mass 8 kg and length 10 m. Find the position of its centre of mass. (Hint: before you begin, mark in the point where the 8 kg acts.)

2   A straight rod *AB* of negligible mass has three masses fixed to it: 4 kg at *A*, 1 kg at a distance 24 cm from *A* and 5 kg at 40 cm from *A*. Find the distance of its centre of mass from *A*.

3   Imagine the *x*-axis. Find the centre of mass of 5 kg at $x = -4$, 3 kg at $x = 1$ and 2 kg at $x = 3$.

4   A cylindrical can of uniform density has a base but no lid. Its base radius is 5 cm and its height is 9 cm. Find the height of its centre of mass.

5   The illustrated 10×8 and 4×6 rectangles are both made of the same uniform material. Find the height of the centre of mass above the base. (Units in cm.)

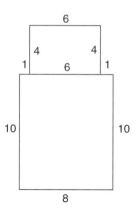

6   A rectangular card of uniform density is 8×18 cm and has a circular hole of radius 4 cm punched in it. Find the height of the centre of mass of the remaining card. (Units in cm.)

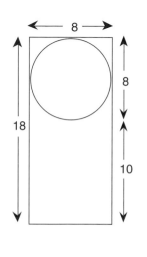

7   Find the centre of mass of these bodies:

(a)   a uniform cube of side 20 mm surmounted symmetrically by another cube of the same material of side 10 mm

(b)   a conical tower of four children's bricks each a circular disc 1 cm thick, the radii of the discs being 4 cm, 3 cm, 2 cm, 1 cm. (All bricks are made of the same uniform material.)

8   Find the coordinates of the centre of mass of the shown F-shaped card (assumed to be made of uniform material). (Units in cm.)

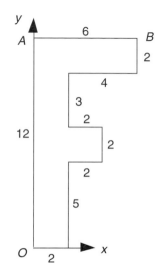

9   If the F-shape in question 8 is made instead from uniform bent wires, where is the centre of mass now?

10   *ABCD* is a uniform rectangular sheet of metal; *AB* = 100 mm and *BC* = 40 mm. Two circular holes are cut, each of radius 10 mm. One has its centre at the mid-point of *AC* and the other touches *BC* at its mid-point. Find the centre of mass of the remaining metal.

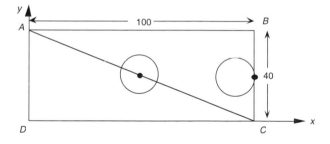

11 The F-shaped card in question 8 is suspended freely from *A*. What angle does *AO* make with the downward vertical?

12 The F-shaped wire in question 9 is suspended freely from *A*. What angle does *AB* make with the downward vertical?

13 The holed sheet in question 10 is suspended freely from *D*. What angle does *DC* make with the downward vertical?

14 Four particles *A*, *B*, *C*, *D* of mass 3, 5, 2, 4 kg are at the points (1, 6), (−1, 5), (2, −3), (−1, −4). Find the coordinates of their centre of mass.

15 The figure shows a lamina which consists of a heavy uniform circular disc centre *X* and radius *R* from which a circular hole centre *Y* and radius *r* has been cut, where $r < R$. The centre of mass of the lamina is at a distance $4/9\,r$ from *X* and $XY = R - r$. By taking moments about *X*, or otherwise, show that $R = \dfrac{5r}{4}$.

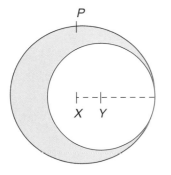

16 The figure shows an earring made from a uniform square lamina *ABCD*, which has each side of length 4 cm. Points *X* and *Y* are on the side *BC* and such that $BX = CY = 1$ cm. The square portion *XYUV* is removed and the resulting earring is suspended from the corner *A*. The earring hangs in equilibrium.

The centre of mass of this earring is *G*.

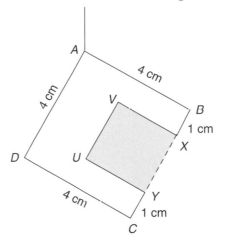

(a) State the distance, in cm, of *G* from *AB*.

(b) Find the distance, in cm, of *G* from *AD*.

(c) Find, to the nearest degree, the acute angle made by *AD* with the downward vertical.

In this section we have:

- solved centre of mass problems by setting up a table and using
$$m_1x_1 + m_2x_2 + \ldots = (m_1 + m_2 + \ldots)\bar{x}$$

- worked out angles, when structures are hanging freely in equilibrium, by remembering that the line joining the point of suspension to the centre of mass will be the downward vertical.

- used given formulae for finding the position of the centre of mass of (uniform) triangular and semi-circular laminas, and solid pyramids, cones and hemispheres.

ANSWERS

Practice questions A

1 4.1 m

2 2.4 m

3 1.6 m

4 $3\frac{1}{21}$ m

5 13

6 $6\frac{2}{3}$

7 1

8 $6\frac{2}{3}$

9 0.6 m

10 $1\frac{1}{3}$ m

Practice questions B

1 $\bar{x} = 3\frac{8}{11}$ m, $\bar{y} = 2\frac{9}{11}$ m

2 $\bar{x} = 3\frac{6}{7}$ m, $\bar{y} = 2\frac{6}{7}$ m

3 $\bar{x} = 2.5$ m, $\bar{y} = 3.5$ m

4 $\bar{x} = 2\frac{2}{3}$ m, $\bar{y} = 3\frac{2}{3}$ m

5 $\bar{x} = 2\frac{5}{7}$ m, $\bar{y} = 7\frac{1}{7}$ m

6 $\bar{x} = 2\frac{5}{9}$ m, $\bar{y} = 6\frac{4}{9}$ m

7 $\bar{x} = 2\frac{1}{2}$ m, $\bar{y} = 2\frac{1}{4}$ m

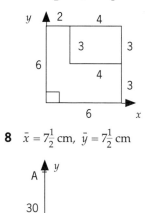

8 $\bar{x} = 7\frac{1}{2}$ cm, $\bar{y} = 7\frac{1}{2}$ cm

9 6.49 cm (2 d.p.), 6.24 cm (2 d.p.)

10 $\bar{x} = 6\frac{2}{5}$ m, $\bar{y} = 1\frac{1}{15}$ m

Practice questions C

1 $\bar{x} = 8$ m, $\bar{y} = 3\frac{1}{3}$ m

2 4 m

3 3 m

4 4.5 cm

5 $\frac{28}{3\pi} \sim 2.97$ cm

6 $\bar{x} = 7\frac{30}{31}$ m, $\bar{y} = 5\frac{13}{31}$ m

7 11.59 m (2 d.p.)

8 8.58 cm (2 d.p.)

9 7.83 cm (2 d.p.)

10 6.77 m (2 d.p.)

Practice questions D

1 $\tan^{-1} 3 \sim 71.6°$

2 (a) 3 cm   (b) 2 cm   (c) 37°

3 $\tan^{-1} 0.75 \sim 37°$

4 (a) 4 cm   (b) 2 cm   (c) $\frac{1}{8}$ M

5 (a) $1\frac{1}{2}$ cm   (b) 1 cm   (c) 56°

6 (a) 1.607 m (3 d.p.)   (b) 15°

7 (a) 44 cm   (b) 52°

8 51°

9 $\tan^{-1}\left(\frac{4}{3\pi}\right) \sim 23°$

10 $\tan^{-1}\left(\frac{3}{8}\right) \sim 21°$

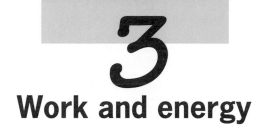

Work and energy

INTRODUCTION Work, energy and power are terms used in everyday life. We say we've done work (or been working) when we have been solving maths problems, or looking after the baby or doing homework. As a result of the work, we say that we have less energy than when we started – and when we've no more energy left, we can do no more work.

Energy, then, is the ability to do work, and when work is done the amount of energy changes.

In this section we'll be looking at the types of energy (kinetic and potential), at work done and at the rate of working, that is, power.

Kinetic energy

OCR M2 5.8.6 (b)

When a body is in motion, the expression:

$\frac{1}{2}$ mass × (velocity)^2

is called the *kinetic energy* of the body. Its unit is the joule.

> kinetic energy $= \frac{1}{2}$ mass × (velocity)^2

Example	A body of mass 5 kg moving initially with velocity 7 m s^{-1} has its velocity reduced to 3 m s^{-1}. Find the loss of kinetic energy.

Solution

K.E. before $= \frac{1}{2} \times 5 \times 7^2 = 122.5$ J

K.E. after $= \frac{1}{2} \times 5 \times 3^2 = 22.5$ J

$\therefore$ Loss of K.E. $= 122.5 - 22.5 = 100$ J

(K.E. is an accepted shorthand for kinetic energy as is J for joules.)

Example A body mass 2 kg moving with velocity 4 m s^{-1} strikes a body mass 3 kg moving with velocity 4 m s^{-1} in the opposite direction. If the heavier body is brought to rest by the collision find:

(a) the velocity of the lighter body after the collision

(b) the total loss of kinetic energy as a result of the impact.

Solution

Figure 3.1

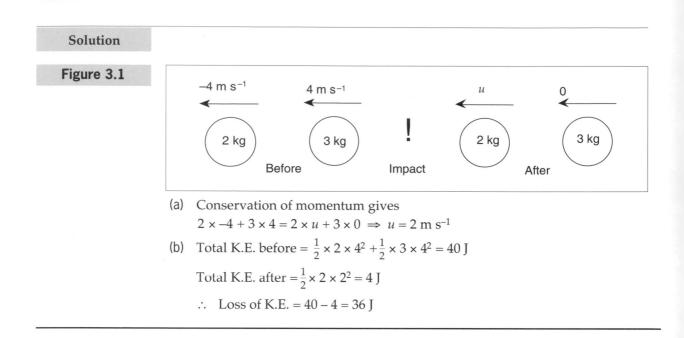

(a)   Conservation of momentum gives

$$2 \times -4 + 3 \times 4 = 2 \times u + 3 \times 0 \implies u = 2 \text{ m s}^{-1}$$

(b)   Total K.E. before $= \frac{1}{2} \times 2 \times 4^2 + \frac{1}{2} \times 3 \times 4^2 = 40 \text{ J}$

Total K.E. after $= \frac{1}{2} \times 2 \times 2^2 = 4 \text{ J}$

$\therefore$ Loss of K.E. $= 40 - 4 = 36 \text{ J}$

Practice questions A

1   A particle of mass 6 kg is moving with velocity 4 m s⁻¹. Find the kinetic energy.

2   A particle of mass 7 kg moving initially with velocity 5 m s⁻¹ has its velocity reduced to 3 m s⁻¹. Find the loss of kinetic energy.

3   A particle of mass 8*m* is moving with velocity 3*u*. Find the kinetic energy.

4   A particle of mass 2 kg, velocity 5 m s⁻¹, strikes a particle mass 3 kg moving with velocity 2 m s⁻¹ in the same direction. After impact the particles coalesce. Find:

(a)   the common velocity of the two particles after impact

(b)   the loss of kinetic energy due to the collision.

5   A particle of mass 6 kg, moving with velocity 8 m s⁻¹, impinges itself directly on a particle of mass 4 kg, moving with a velocity of 5 m s⁻¹ in the opposite direction. The particles coalesce after impact. Find:

(a)   the common velocity of the two particles after impact

(b)   the loss of kinetic energy due to the collision

6   A particle of mass 12 kg has velocity vector $(7\mathbf{i} + 24\mathbf{j})$ m s⁻¹. Find its kinetic energy.

7   At time *t*, a particle of mass 12 kg has position vector $(6t\mathbf{i} + 8t\mathbf{j})$ m. Show the particle is moving with constant speed and find its kinetic energy.

8   At time *t*, a particle of mass 8 kg has position vector $(t^2\mathbf{i} + 3t\mathbf{j})$ m. Find the speed and kinetic energy of the particle when $t = 2$.

9   A particle *A* of mass 4*m* is moving in a straight line on a horizontal table. It collides with another particle *B* of mass *m* moving in the same straight line on the table. Immediately before the collision, the speed of *A* is 3*u*, the speed of *B* is *u*, and the particles are moving directly towards each other. In the collision the two particles coalesce to form a single particle *C*. Find:

(a)   the speed of *C* immediately after the collision

(b)   the kinetic energy lost in the collision

10   A particle of mass 6 kg, moving with velocity $(\mathbf{i} + 2\mathbf{j})$ m s⁻¹, impinges itself directly on a particle of mass 4 kg, moving with velocity $(0.5\mathbf{i} - 0.75\mathbf{j})$ m s⁻¹. In the collision the two particles coalesce to form a single particle *P*. Find:

(a)   the speed of *P* immediately after the collision

(b)   the kinetic energy lost in the collision.

Work done by a force

One of the five constant acceleration equations you met in Section 2 of Unit M1 gives us:

$$v^2 = u^2 + 2as \Rightarrow \tfrac{1}{2}v^2 - \tfrac{1}{2}u^2 = as$$

Multiplying through by m and then using $F = ma$, this gives us:

$$\tfrac{1}{2}mv^2 - \tfrac{1}{2}mu^2 = Fs.$$

But the left-hand side of this equation is the gain in kinetic energy.

∴   Gain in K.E. = Force × distance moved

But force × distance is defined as the work done by the force:

> Gain in K.E. = Force × distance moved = Work done by force

It follows that the unit of work done is the joule (J).

Example

A 1500 kg car starts from rest and reaches a speed of 20 m s⁻¹ after travelling 300 m. Neglecting resistances, find the constant driving force.

Solution

Gain in K.E. $= \tfrac{1}{2} \times 1500 \times 20^2 = 300\,000$ J

Since distance covered is 300 m,

Force × 300 = 300 000 ⇒ $F = 1000$

(An alternative method would be to use $v^2 = u^2 + 2as$ to find the acceleration a [you get $\tfrac{2}{3}$ m s⁻²] and then say $F = ma$. Use this method if you prefer.)

This constant driving force of the car is called its *tractive force*.

∴ The car has a tractive force of 1000 N.

Example

A body of mass 20 kg has velocity 20 m s⁻¹ at the foot of a rough plane inclined at 30° to the horizontal, and 2 m s⁻¹ when it has travelled 40 m up the plane. Find the constant frictional force exerted by the plane on the body.

Solution

Loss in K.E. $= \tfrac{1}{2} \times 20 \times 20^2 - \tfrac{1}{2} \times 20 \times 2^2 = 3960$

Component of weight down the plane

$= 20 \times 9.8 \times \sin 30° = 98$ N.

(See Exercise 8 in Section 4 of M1 (p. 75) if you need a refresher here.)

If the frictional force down the plane is F, then:

$(F + 98) \times 40 = 3960 \Rightarrow F = 1$

∴ The frictional force exerted by the plane = 1 N.

Practice questions B

1 What is the work done in increasing the speed of a particle, of mass 7 kg, from 5 m s^{-1} to 9 m s^{-1}?

2 A particle of mass 12 kg, initially at rest, has its speed increased to 4 m s^{-1}. What is the work done?

3 A 16 kg particle is initially at rest. A constant tractive force F N is then applied to the particle so that, after covering a distance of 12 m, its velocity is 6 m s^{-1}. Find F.

4 An 8 kg particle is initially moving with velocity 7 m s^{-1}. A constant tractive force F N is then applied to the particle (in the same direction as the initial velocity) so that, after covering a distance of 20 m, the particle has a velocity of 11 m s^{-1}. Find F.

5 A particle of mass 60 kg has velocity 30 m s^{-1} at the foot of a rough plane, inclined at 30° to the horizontal. It comes to rest after travelling 10 m up the plane. Find the constant frictional force exerted by the plane on the particle.

6 A small block is pulled along a rough horizontal floor at a constant speed of 2 m s^{-1} by a force which has constant magnitude 30 N and acts at constant angle θ to the horizontal. Given that the work done by the force in 30 seconds is 900 J, calculate the value of θ.

7 A bus of mass 15 000 kg moves up a straight hill inclined at an angle α to the horizontal, where $\sin \alpha = 0.4$, at a constant speed of 15 m s^{-1}. The resistance to motion has magnitude 170 000 N. Find the work done each second by the engine of the bus.

8 One end of a light inextensible string is attached to a ring which is threaded on a fixed horizontal bar. The string is taut and is inclined at a constant angle of 30° to the bar, as shown below:

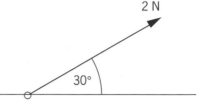

Given that the tension on the string is constant and equal to 2 N, calculate the work done by the tension as the ring travels a distance of 2 m along the bar.

9 A car of mass 800 kg descends a straight hill which is inclined at an angle of 2° to the horizontal. The car passes through the points P and Q with speeds of 10 m s^{-1} and 32 m s^{-1} respectively. The distance PQ is 500 m. Assuming there are no resistances to motion, calculate the work done by the car's engine for the journey from P to Q.

10 A 10 kg body is being dragged up a plane, inclined at an angle α to the horizontal, where $\sin \alpha = 0.2$, at a steady speed of 5 m s^{-1}. The frictional resistances to motion are 10.4 N. What is the work done in dragging the body up the plane for 4 seconds?

Potential energy

OCR M2 5.8.6 (b),(c),(e)

Imagine a particle of mass m falling freely through the air. Suppose that at heights h_1 and h_2 its downward speeds are v_1 and v_2 respectively.

Figure 3.2

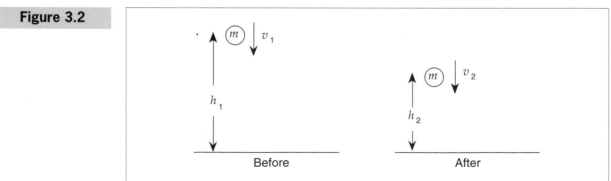

The force acting on the mass is mg and the distance covered is $h_1 - h_2$.

∴   Using the rule work done = gain in K.E. we get:

$$mg(h_1 - h_2) = \tfrac{1}{2}\,mv_2{}^2 - \tfrac{1}{2}\,mv_1{}^2$$

This rearranges to give:

$$\tfrac{1}{2}\,mv_1{}^2 + mgh_1 = \tfrac{1}{2}mv_2{}^2 + mgh_2$$

The quantities mgh_1 and mgh_2 are called *potential energy* (or P.E. for short).

∴   In this case K.E. + P.E. gives the same answer both before and after, i.e. *in this case K.E. + P.E. is a constant.* This is known as **the principle of conservation of energy**.

It can be proved that if a particle goes down a smooth slope or any smooth curve, then K.E. + P.E. remains constant. The crucial thing to remember is that *it must be smooth* and that the only forces acting are the weight and normal reaction to it.

Example	A particle of mass 6 kg is 8 m above a fixed horizontal surface. Taking that surface as having zero potential energy, find the potential energy of the particle.
Solution	See Fig. 3.3

Figure 3.3

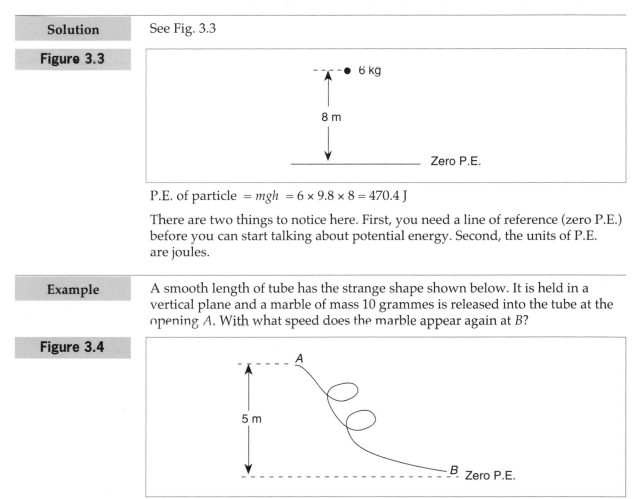

P.E. of particle $= mgh = 6 \times 9.8 \times 8 = 470.4$ J

There are two things to notice here. First, you need a line of reference (zero P.E.) before you can start talking about potential energy. Second, the units of P.E. are joules.

Example	A smooth length of tube has the strange shape shown below. It is held in a vertical plane and a marble of mass 10 grammes is released into the tube at the opening A. With what speed does the marble appear again at B?

Figure 3.4

Solution	The tube is smooth $\therefore$ we can use the rule K.E. + P.E. = constant.

$$\therefore \quad \tfrac{1}{2} \times 0.01 \times 0^2 + 0.01 \times 9.8 \times 5 = \tfrac{1}{2} \times 0.01 \times v^2 + 0$$

(I've taken the lower level as having zero P.E.)

$\Rightarrow \quad 0.49 = 0.005v^2 \Rightarrow v = 9.9$ (1 d.p.)

$\therefore$ The marble appears with a speed of 9.9 m s^{-1}.

(If you go on to study Unit M3, then you'll meet this idea again when tackling circular motion.)

Example	A particle P of mass 5 kg is suspended at the end of a light string of length 0.6 m which is fixed at the other end O. The particle is held with the string taut at an angle of 40° to the downward vertical and let go (see Fig. 3.5).

Figure 3.5	

What is the maximum velocity of the particle in the ensuing pendulum motion?

Solution	The particle will have maximum velocity when it is at the lowest point, L, in its path. At that point its kinetic energy will be $\tfrac{1}{2} \times 5 \times v^2 = 2.5v^2$ where v is the maximum velocity.

Taking the level of L as zero potential energy, the potential energy of the particle at P will be $5 \times 9.8 \times DL$.

But $DL = OL - OD$.

$\therefore \quad DL = 0.6 - 0.6 \cos 40° = 0.6 (1 - \cos 40°)$.

$\therefore$ The potential energy at P is $5 \times 9.8 \times 0.6 (1 - \cos 40°)$

Since no energy is lost, we can use the rule K.E. + P.E. = constant.

$\therefore$ Total energy at L = Total energy at P.

$\therefore \quad 2.5v^2 = 5 \times 9.8 \times 0.6 (1 - \cos 40°)$

$\therefore \quad 2.5v^2 \doteq 6.878$

$\therefore \quad v = 1.66$

$\therefore$ The maximum velocity is 1.66 m s^{-1} (2 d.p.).

Example	A trolley of mass 200 kg is travelling in a straight line on level ground with a speed of 25 m s^{-1}. After a distance of 10 m the ground slopes upwards at an angle of 30° to the horizontal. The frictional resistance of the ground is 400 N. How far up the slope will the trolley travel before coming to rest?

Solution

Figure 3.6

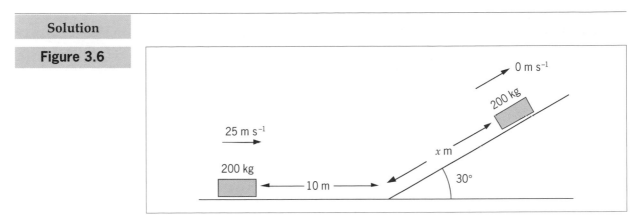

The initial K.E. $= \frac{1}{2} \times 200 \times 25^2 = 62\,500$ J.

Taking the level ground as zero P.E., the P.E. of the trolley when it stops is given by

P.E. $= 200 \times 9.8 \times x \sin 30°$,   when x is the distance travelled up the slope

The work done against the frictional resistance is given by

Work done $= 400 \times (10 + x)$

∴   Using the rule: initial energy = final energy + work done
     we get $62\,500 = 200 \times 9.8 \times x \sin 30° + 400 \times (10 + x)$

∴ $62\,500 = 980x + 4000 + 400x$

∴ $58\,500 = 1380x$

∴ $x = 42.4$

∴   The trolley travels 42.4 m (1 d.p.) up the slope before coming to rest.

Practice questions C

1 A particle of mass 12 kg is 9 m above a fixed horizontal surface. Taking that surface as having zero potential energy, find the potential energy of the particle.

2 A particle of mass 5 kg is released from rest on a smooth plane inclined at 30° to the horizontal. After travelling a distance of 20 m down the plane, the particle achieves a speed of v m s^{-1}. Use the principle of conservation of energy to find v.

3 A car of mass 1300 kg drives up a straight road inclined at an angle α to the horizontal, where $\sin \alpha = \frac{1}{13}$. It passes a point A on the road with a speed of 20 m s^{-1}, and a point B, higher up the road, with a speed of 5 m s^{-1}, where the distance from A to B is 200 m.

(a) Find the change in total energy of the car as it moves from A to B.

(b) State whether the change is an increase of decrease.

4 A pendulum consists of a light string 8 m long attached to a particle of mass 12 kg and can swing freely. It is held taut at an angle of 60° to the downward vertical and released. Find the velocity of the mass at its lowest point.

5 A mass of 8 kg suspended by a light string 10 m long and at rest is projected horizontally with a velocity of 7 m s^{-1}. Find the angle made by the string with the downward vertical when the mass comes to momentary rest.

6 Masses of 12 kg and 8 kg are connected by a light string passing over a smooth pulley. After the 12 kg mass descends from rest for a time of 4 seconds, find:

(a) the velocity of each mass

(b) the potential energy lost by the system.

7   A boy slides down a sloping chute into a swimming pool. He starts from rest at a vertical height of 4 m above the water. The chute is perfectly smooth. By modelling the boy as a particle, find the speed with which he enters the water.

If the chute is not smooth and if the boy, who weighs 50 kg dissipates 960 J of energy in overcoming the friction of the chute, find the speed with which he enters the water.

8   A girl weighing 50 kg slides down a rope from rest at a height of 6 m and reaches the floor with a velocity of 6 m s^{-1}. How much energy is lost on her striking the floor, and how much is lost in friction against the rope?

9   Two pendulums with light strings each 0.8 m long carry masses of 1.5 kg and 2.5 kg and are suspended side by side from the same point. The larger mass is raised until the string is horizontal and taut and is then released.

If the two masses stick together on impact, find the vertical height to which they rise after the impact.

10 A truck of mass 150 kg is travelling in a straight line on level ground with a speed of 25 m s^{-1}. After a distance of 40 m the ground slopes upwards at an angle of 30° to the horizontal. The frictional resistance of the ground is 750 N. How far up the slope will the truck travel before coming to rest?

Power

OCR M2 5.8.6 (d)

Power is the rate at which work is done.

Now work $W = Fs$, where the force F is constant.

$$\therefore \quad \text{Power} = \frac{dW}{dt} = \frac{d}{dt}(Fs) = F\frac{ds}{dt} = Fv \quad \text{(where } F \text{ is a } constant \text{ force)}$$

Power = force × velocity (for constant force)

and the unit of power is the watt, written W.

Example	Find the power necessary for a train of mass 4×10^5 kg to travel at 80 km h^{-1} against resistance of 60 N per 10^3 kg.

Solution	Resisting force = $400 \times 60 = 24\,000$ N

Travelling at constant speed $\therefore$ tractive force of the engine is also 24 000 N

Also $80 \text{ km h}^{-1} = \frac{80}{18} \times 5 = 22\frac{2}{9} \text{ m s}^{-1}$

using the rule 18 km h^{-1} = 5 m s^{-1}. See Section 2 of Unit M1 if you've forgotten.

$\therefore \quad$ Power $= 24\,000 \times 22\frac{2}{9} = 533\,000$ W (3 s.f.) = 533 kW

Example	A train of mass 500 000 kg is travelling at 30 m s^{-1} up a slope of 1 in 100. The frictional resistance is 50 N per 1000 kg. Find the rate at which the engine is working.

Solution	Component of weight down the plane

$$= 500\,000 \times 9.8 \times \frac{1}{100} = 49\,000 \text{ N}$$

(See Exercise 8, in Unit M1 Section 4 (p. 75), if necessary. Also:

'a slope of 1 in 100' $\Rightarrow$ 100   1 θ $\Rightarrow = \sin\theta = \frac{1}{100}$)

Frictional force down plane	$= 500 \times 50$	$= 25\ 000$ N
$\therefore$ Tractive force of the engine	$= 49\ 000 + 25\ 000$	$= 74\ 000$ N
$\therefore$ Rate of working = power	$= 74\ 000 \times 30$	$= \underline{2220}$ kW.

Example

The total mass of a train is 2×10^5 kg and the total resistances to motion amount to $\frac{1}{200}$ of the total weight. What is the power of the engine if it can just keep the train moving at a uniform speed of 108 km h^{-1} on the level?

Solution

Total resistance to motion $= \frac{1}{200} \times 2 \times 10^5 \times 9.8$ N $= 9800$ N.

The speed is uniform $\therefore$ the tractive force of the engine must also equal 9800 N.

The speed is 108 km h^{-1} = 108 $\times \frac{5}{18}$ m s^{-1} = 30 m s^{-1}

$\therefore$ Power $= 9800 \times 30 = 294\ 000$ W

$\therefore$ The power of the engine is 294 kW.

Example

An engine of 245 kW is taking a train of mass 2×10^5 kg up an incline of 1 in 250, and the resistance equals 3000 N. What is the maximum uniform speed of the train in km h^{-1}?

Solution

Component of weight down the slope $= 2 \times 10^5 \times 9.8 \times \frac{1}{250}$ N $= 7840$ N

$\therefore$ Total resistance to motion $= (7840 + 3000)$ N $= 10\ 840$ N

The speed is uniform $\therefore$ the tractive force of the engine must also equal 10 840 N.

$\therefore$ Power $= 245$ kW $\Rightarrow 245\ 000 = 10840v$, where v is the uniform speed

$\therefore$ $v = 22.60$ m s^{-1} or $22.60 \times \frac{18}{5} = 81.4$ km h^{-1}

$\therefore$ The maximum uniform speed is 81.4 km h^{-1}.

Example

A pump raises water from a depth of 20 m and delivers it at a rate 0.15 m^3 s^{-1} at a speed of 12 m s^{-1}. Find the power of the pump.

Solution

Taking 1 m^3 of water as weighing 1000 kg, the mass of water delivered per second is $0.15 \times 1000 = 150$ kg.

The work done in *1 second* in raising the water from a depth of 20 m is $150 \times 9.8 \times 20 = 29400$ J.

The kinetic energy of the water delivered in *1 second* is $\frac{1}{2} \times 150 \times 12^2 = 10\ 800$ J.

$\therefore$ The total amount of work done in *1 second* is $29400 + 10\ 800 = 40\ 200$ J

$\therefore$ The power of the pump $= 40\ 200$ W, i.e. 40.2 kW.

Example	The engine of a car is working at a steady rate of 4.5 kW. The car of mass 1100 kg is being driven along a level road against a constant reistance to motion of 400 N. Find the acceleration of the car when its speed is 9 m s^{-1}.
Solution	Power is 4.5 kW = 4500 W and speed is 9 m s^{-1}.

$\therefore$ The tractive force F of the engine is given by

$4500 = F \times 9 \quad \Rightarrow F = 500$ N

But the resistance to motion is 400 N.

$\therefore$ Newton's Second Law (see Section 3 in Unit M1) gives

$500 - 400 = 1100a \quad \Rightarrow a = \dfrac{1}{11}$

$\therefore$ The acceleration of the car is $\dfrac{1}{11}$ m s^{-2}. |
| **Example** | With its engine working at a constant rate of 12 kW, a car of mass 900 kg ascends a hill of 1 in 49 against a constant resistance to motion of 420 N.

Find the acceleration of the car up the hill when travelling with a speed of 5 m s^{-1}. |
| **Solution** | The weight of the car = 900 × 9.8 N.

$\therefore$ The component of weight down the plane = $900 \times 9.8 \times \dfrac{1}{49} = 180$ N

Since other resistances to motion total 420 N, the total force down the plane against the motion = 420 + 180 = 600 N ... ①

If the tractive force of the engine is F then, since the power is 12 000 W and the speed is 5 m s^{-1}, it follows that

$12\,000 = F \times 5 \Rightarrow F = 2400$ N   ... ②

Using ① and ②, Newton's Second Law gives

$2400 - 600 = 900a \quad \Rightarrow a = 2$

$\therefore$ The acceleration of the car is 2 m s^{-2}. |

Practice questions D

1 A car of weight 13 000 N travels at a constant speed up a straight hill inclined at 3° to the horizontal. The car's engine works at a constant rate of 40 kW. Assuming there is a resistance to motion of magnitude 1200 N acting on the car, find the speed.

2 If a car travels at a steady speed of 10 m s^{-1} against resistances of 300 N, what power is being exerted by the engine?

3 A girl of mass 50 kg walks up a flight of stairs of vertical height 3 m in 6 seconds. What power is she sustaining?

4 It took me 40 seconds to run a distance of 200 m. If the resistances to motion are estimated as 100 N, what power did I use?

5 The power of the engine of a car is 8 kW. What would be the maximum speed of the car on the level against resistances of 200 N?

6 A train of total mass 250 tonnes travels at a constant speed of 15 m s^{-1} on the level, the resistances being 30 000 N. What is the power of the engine?

7 A car of mass 900 kg is travelling at a steady speed of 15 m s^{-1} on the level. The engine is developing a power of 9 kW. Find the resistance to motion.

8 A pump raises water through a height of 25 m at a rate of 0.02 m^3 per second. What is the power of the pump? (1 m^3 of water has mass 1000 kg.)

9 A fire hose delivers water horizontally at a speed of 30 m s^{-1} through a nozzle of cross-sectional area 8 cm^2. Find the power of the pump if it is only 60% efficient.

10 A car of mass 900 kg working at 14 kW can climb a slope of 1 in 70 at a steady speed of 25 m s^{-1}. What is the resistance due to motion? If the resistance and the power are unchanged, what would be the maximum speed of the car on level ground?

11 A cyclist and his bike have a combined mass of 80 kg. Find the maximum speed that the cyclist can attain on level ground when working at a constant rate of 180 W against resistances totalling 30 N.

The cyclist now ascends a slope of 1 in 16. The rate of working is unchanged, but the resistances are now 41 N. Find the maximum speed of the cyclist up the slope.

12 With its engine working at a constant rate of 14 kW, a car of mass 700 kg ascends a hill of 1 in 7 against a constant resistance to motion of 1270 N. Find:

(a) the acceleration of the car up the hill when travelling with a speed of 3.5 m s^{-1}

(b) the maximum speed of the car up the hill.

13 When a car of mass 800 kg has its engine working at a constant rate of 8 kW, the car can ascend a hill of 1 in 56 at a constant speed of 20 m s^{-1}. Find:

(a) the resistance to motion experienced by the car

(b) the maximum speed of the car when travelling down the same slope with the resistance to motion unchanged, but with the engine working at a reduced rate of 3 kW

SUMMARY EXERCISE

1 A body of mass 8 kg increases its speed from 4 m s^{-1} to 6 m s^{-1}. What is the gain in kinetic energy?

2 A body mass 225 kg velocity 4 m s^{-1} strikes a body mass 75 kg initially at rest. If the bodies move away together find:

(a) their common velocity

(b) the total loss of kinetic energy during the impact.

3 A 70 kg cyclist on a 30 kg bike starts from rest at A. His driving force on the bicycle is 696 N and the resistance to motion is 196 N.

(a) What is the acceleration of the bicycle?

(b) What is the cyclist's speed at B (40 m ahead of A)?

When the cyclist reaches B a 10 kg lump of soft clay hits him in the eyes and sticks to his goggles. At impact the clay is flying at 35 m s^{-1} towards the bicycle.

(c) What is the speed of the cyclist after impact?

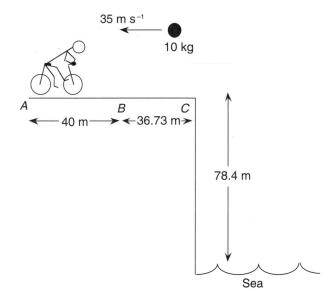

Not being able to see, he stops pedalling but, having no brakes, has to rely on friction to slow him down.

(d) What is his retardation?

(e) What is his speed when he reaches the cliff's edge at C (36.73 m from B)?

The bicycle now flies straight off the cliff's edge into the sea.

(f) How long does it take him to hit the water?

(g) How far out does he hit the sea?

(h) What is his speed (in magnitude and direction) as he begins to sink?

(i) How much kinetic energy has been gained from just before impact with the clay until he begins to sink?

4 A small sphere R of mass 0.08 kg, moving with a speed 1.5 m/s, collides directly with another small sphere S, of mass 0.12 kg, moving in the same direction with speed 1 m/s. Immediately after the collision R and S continue to move in the same direction with speeds u m/s and v m/s respectively. Given that $u : v = 21 : 26$,

(a) show that $v = 1.3$

(b) find the magnitude of the impulse, in N s, received by R as a result of the collision.

5 Assuming the mass of 1 m^3 of water is 1000 kg, find the work done in giving 1 m^3 of water a velocity of 8 m s^{-1}.

6 Find the work done in raising a body of mass 50 kg a distance of 8 m into a space craft stationary on the surface of the moon. (Take the moon's gravity to be 1.65 m s^{-2}.)

7 A boy of mass 40 kg slides down a rough chute inclined at 60° to the horizontal. If the boy starts from rest and if there is a constant frictional resistance of 60 N, with what velocity will he pass the point 10 m from his starting point?

8 A bullet of mass 10 grammes, velocity 600 m s^{-1}, enters 2.4 m into the protective sandbags before coming to rest. What is the resisting force of the sandbags (assumed constant)?

9 A body of mass 20 kg slides down a smooth plane inclined at 30° to the horizontal. Initially it is at rest. What is its speed when it has travelled 5 m down the plane?

10 A smooth particle of mass 0.02 kg is thrown into the tubular contraption shown at the top of the next column with an initial speed of 3 m s^{-1}. With what speed does it come flying out of the hole H?

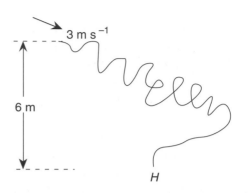

(Assume that the smooth tube is one continuous length and that it is held in a vertical plane.)

11 A disused and damaged (but smooth) fairground switchback has a vertical cross-section as shown below:

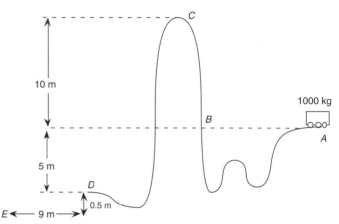

The switchback is continuous from A to D but there is a 0.5 m drop and a 9 m gap from D to E. A 1000 kg car is stationary at A.

(a) The car slips down on to the switchback. What happens?

(b) If instead the car has an initial velocity of 6 m s^{-1}, what happens now?

(c) What happens to the car if its initial velocity is 15 m s^{-1}?

12 A crane raises a 5000 kg steel girder at 0.4 m s^{-1}. Assuming that work is not lost in driving the crane, what is the power of the crane's engine?

13 A machine for firing clay pigeons throws 3 'birds' a minute. The mass of each 'bird' is 0.08 kg and the velocity with which each leaves the machine is 20 m s^{-1}. Find the power necessary to drive the machine assuming half of it is lost in the machine.

14 Find the kW used by a fire pump which raises water a distance of 4 m and delivers 0.12 m^3 a minute at a speed of 10 m s^{-1}. (Assume that 1 m^3 of water weighs 1000 kg.)

15 A car mass 800 kg ascends a hill of 1 in 10 at 20 m s^{-1}, the air resistance being 200 N. What power is the engine producing?

16 A light motorcycle whose mass including rider is 200 kg can go at 10 m s^{-1} up a plane of inclination θ, where $\sin \theta = \frac{1}{14}$ and at 20 m s^{-1} down the same plane. If the resistance varies as the square of the speed and the power developed by the machine is constant, find the power developed.

17 The engine of a 5000 kg coach can work at 40 kW. If the resistance to motion is 1500 N, find the maximum speed:

(a) along the level

(b) up a slope of angle θ, where $\sin \theta = \frac{1}{98}$.

18 A car of mass 900 kg pulls a trailer of mass 350 kg along a straight level road against a total resistance of 1250 N. Given that the car is using its full power of 45 kW, show that its acceleration is 1.4 m s^{-2} when its speed is 54 km h^{-1}.

Find also the tension in the coupling between the car and the trailer at this speed, assuming that the total resistance is divided between the car and the trailer in the ratio of their masses.

19 A locomotive working at the rate of 240 kW pulls a train of total mass 56 000 kg (including the locomotive) up a straight track inclined to the horizontal at an angle θ, where $\sin \theta = \frac{1}{50}$.

When the speed is 5 m s^{-1}, the acceleration is $\frac{1}{4} \text{ m s}^{-2}$. Find the total resistance at this speed.

20 A boy and his bicycle have a total mass of 60 kg. When he is working at a rate of 400 W his maximum speed on a level road is 5 m/s.

(a) Calculate the frictional resistance.

The boy ascends a slope inclined at an angle α to the horizontal where $\sin \alpha = \frac{1}{12}$. His work rate remains the same but the frictional resistance is now 110 N.

(b) Calculate his maximum speed up the slope.

The bicycle will overturn if its speed drops below 2 m/s.

(c) Calculate the angle of the steepest slope the boy can ascend, assuming that the frictional resistance is still 110 N, and his work rate is still the same.

21 A car of mass 560 kg is pulling a caravan of mass 240 kg along a horizontal road. There are constant resistances of 120 N to the motion of the car and 80 N to the motion of the caravan.

Given that the tractive force of the car is 1200 N, calculate:

(a) the acceleration of the car and caravan

(b) the tension in the tow-bar

(c) the power of the car's engine when the speed is 12 m s^{-1}.

The car now pulls the caravan up a road inclined at θ to the horizontal, where $\sin \theta = \frac{1}{16}$. Assuming that the tractive force and the resistances are unchanged:

(d) calculate the acceleration of the car and caravan

(e) show that the tension in the tow-bar is unchanged.

22 The magnitude of the resistance to the motion of a motor coach is K newtons per tonne, where K is a constant. The motor coach has mass $4\frac{1}{2}$ tonnes.

When travelling on a straight horizontal road with the engine working at 39.6 kW, the coach maintains a steady speed of 40 m/s.

(a) Show that $K = 220$.

The motor coach ascends a straight road, which is inclined at an angle α to the horizontal, where $\sin \alpha = 0.3$ with the same power output and against the same constant resisting forces.

(b) Find, in joules to 2 s.f., the kinetic energy of the motor coach when it is travelling at its maximum speed up the slope.

SUMMARY

In this section we have seen that:

- kinetic energy = $\frac{1}{2}$ mass × (velocity)^2 and it is measured in joules (J)
- there is a loss of total kinetic energy during any collision
- work done = force × distance (where the force is constant) = Fs
- the unit of work done is the joule
- work done = gain in K.E.

  $\therefore\ Fs = \frac{1}{2}mv^2 - \frac{1}{2}mu^2$

- potential energy is *mgh*, when *h* is measured from some agreed level
- the unit of P.E. is the joule
- on smooth surfaces K.E. + P.E. = constant

  $\therefore\ \frac{1}{2}mv_1^2 + mgh_1 = \frac{1}{2}mv_2^2 + mgh_2$

- the principle of the conservation of energy tells us that:

  the (K.E. + P.E.) of a body at any time $\quad=\quad$ original (K.E. + P.E.) $\quad+\quad$ any work done by a force acting on the body.

- power is the rate of doing work
- the unit of power is the watt (W)
- power = force × velocity (where the force is constant) = number of joules per second (J s^{-1})
- the driving force of an engine is known as its tractive force.

ANSWERS

Practice questions A

1 48 J   2 56 J   3 $36mu^2$

4 (a) 3.2 m s^{-1} (b) 5.4 J

5 (a) 2.8 m s^{-1} (b) 202.8 J

6 3750 J

7 Speed of 10 m s^{-1}. K.E. = 600 J

8 5 m s^{-1}, 100 J

9 (a) 2.2*u*   (b) $6.4mu^2$

10 (a) 1.7 m s^{-1} (b) 2.175 J

Practice questions B

1 196 J   2 96 J   3 24

4 14.4   5 2406 N   6 60°

7 3432 kJ   8 $2\sqrt{3}$ N ~ 3.46 N

9 232.8 kJ   10 600 J

Practice questions C

1 1058.4 J

2 $5 \times 9.8 \times 20 \sin 30° = \frac{1}{2} \times 5 \times v^2 \quad \therefore v = 14$

3 (a) 47.75 kJ   (b) decrease

4 $\sqrt{8g}$ ~ 8.85 m s^{-1} 5 $\cos^{-1} 0.75$ ~ 41.4°

6 (a) 7.84 m s^{-1} (b) 614.656 J

7 8.85 m s^{-1} (2 d.p.), $\sqrt{40}$ ~ 6.32 m s^{-1} (2 d.p.)

8 900 J, 2040 J   9 $\frac{5}{16}$ m

10 11.4 m (1 d.p.)

Practice questions D

1 21.3 m s^{-1} (1 d.p.)   2 3 kW

3 245 W   4 500 W   5 40 m s^{-1}

6 450 kW   7 600 N   8 4900 W

9 18 kW   10 434 N, 32.3 m s^{-1} (1 d.p.)

11 6 m s^{-1}, 2 m s^{-1} 12 2.5 m s^{-2}, $6\frac{2}{9}$ m s^{-1}

13 260 N, 25 m s^{-1}

Collisions

INTRODUCTION   When two objects collide, we have seen from our work on this topic in Unit M1 that momentum is conserved: applying this principle gives us one equation connecting the velocities before and after the collision. In order to solve more general systems we need a further equation. This comes from applying Newton's Experimental Law, which states that in a collision between two objects

$$\frac{\text{speed of separation}}{\text{speed of approach}} = e$$

where e is a constant for any two bodies called the **coefficient of restitution**. Most of the work in this section will deal with solving problems by finding equations coming from these two sources.

For your work on this section you will need to be familiar with:

● simultaneous equations

● the work on momentum in Unit M1 (Section 3).

Coefficient of restitution (e)

OCR M2 5.8.5 (a),(b),(c)

This measures the elasticity of the two bodies and takes a value between 0 and 1. If $e = 0$, the bodies are said to be **perfectly inelastic** and if $e = 1$, the bodies are said to be **perfectly elastic**.

One of the simplest examples of this is a moving particle colliding with a fixed surface with velocity u, where the coefficient of restitution between the particle and surface is e. If the velocity with which the particle rebounds is v, then by Newton's Experimental Law,

$$\frac{\text{Speed of separation (i.e. relative speed)}}{\text{Speed of approach (i.e. relative speed)}} = \frac{v}{u} = e$$

$$\text{i.e. } v = eu$$

Here's an example of this.

| Example | A sphere of mass m is dropped from a height of h on to a horizontal floor. Find the height to which the sphere rebounds if the coefficient of restitution between sphere and floor is $\frac{1}{2}$. |

| Solution | We can find the velocity of the sphere immediately before the collision by equating the loss in potential energy with the gain in kinetic energy. |

| Figure 4.1 | |

$$\therefore \quad \frac{1}{2}mu^2 = mgh \implies u^2 = 2gh$$

$\implies \quad u = \sqrt{2gh}$, the velocity before the collision

The velocity v after the collision is given by eu,

i.e. $e\sqrt{2gh}$ or $\frac{1}{2}\sqrt{2gh}$, since $e = \frac{1}{2}$

This gives the new kinetic energy as

$$\frac{1}{2}mv^2 = \frac{1}{2}m \times \left[\frac{1}{2}\sqrt{2gh}\right]^2 = \frac{1}{2}m \times \frac{1}{4}2gh = \frac{mgh}{4}$$

For maximum height, this kinetic energy will all be converted into potential energy. If the height is H, the potential energy will be mgH and so:

$$mgH = mg\frac{h}{4} \implies H = \frac{h}{4}$$

i.e. the sphere will rebound to one quarter of its original height.

Practice questions A

1 (a) A particle mass m falls directly on to a horizontal floor. At impact the speed of the particle is u. If the coefficient of restitution between the particle and the floor is e, with what speed does the particle rebound?

   (b) A particle of mass m is moving in a straight line directly towards a fixed vertical wall. If the coefficient of restitution between the particle and the wall is e and if, at impact, the speed of the particle is u, with what speed does the particle rebound?

2 A ball is dropped from a gallery 10 m above the floor. If $e = 0.6$, find how high it rises after the first bounce.

3 A ball is dropped on a paving slab and rises again to a height of one-third of that from which it fell. Find the coefficient of restitution.

4 A ball is thrown vertically downwards on to the ground from a height of 0.9 m, and rises again to this height after the first bounce. If $e = 0.6$, find the speed with which it was thrown.

5 The coefficient of restitution between a golf ball and a concrete floor is 0.9. When the ball is dropped from a height of 3 m, what is its speed immediately after impact?

   What is the height of the first rebound?

6 A ball is dropped from a height of 2.5 m and rebounds to a height of 1.6 m. What is the coefficient of restitution?

7 A particle is dropped on to a horizontal floor and rebounds to a height of 0.24 m. If the coefficient of restitution between the particle and the floor is 0.93, what was the speed of the particle immediately before impact?

8 A marble dropped on a stone floor from a height of 3 m is found to rebound to a height of 2.5 m. Find the coefficient of restitution correct to 2 d.p.

9 A particle is dropped from a height of 4 m on to an elastic horizontal plane and just before the third impact with the plane it has described a total distance of 6.5 m. Calculate the coefficient of restitution.

10 A particle of mass 10 kg hangs freely by a light inextensible string of length 5 m from a point on a smooth vertical plane. It is drawn aside so that the string is taut and makes an angle of 60° with the plane, and released to strike the plane at right angles.

(a) Show that the particle hits the plane with a speed of 7 m s^{-1}.

After impact the particle rises until the string makes an angle of 30° with the plane.

(b) Find the coefficient of restitution between the particle and the plane.

Examples involving collisions

Here is an example of a more practical situation where we model cars by particles and apply our equations to these.

Example

A queue of cars is stationary when the last one is hit in the rear by another car. The situation is modelled by a series of stationary particles each of mass 1500 kg lying in a straight line, the last one of which is struck by another particle of the same mass travelling with a speed of 40 km per hour along the line of stationary particles. The coefficient of restitution between any of the particles is e and it is assumed that the particles move with constant velocity between impacts.

Find the speed of the car which was originally next to last in the queue after it has been struck by the one behind.

Modern cars tend to be designed with 'crumple zones' at the front and rear which collapse on impact from these directions and help to absorb the energy of a collision. Determine, with reasons, whether such 'crumple zones' are modelled by a high or low value of e.

Solution

We draw a sketch and put in the usual information.

Figure 4.2

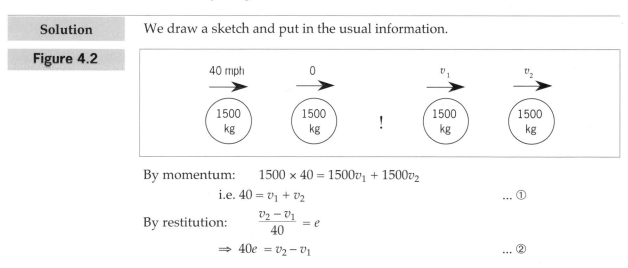

By momentum: $1500 \times 40 = 1500v_1 + 1500v_2$

i.e. $40 = v_1 + v_2$ ... ①

By restitution: $\dfrac{v_2 - v_1}{40} = e$

$\Rightarrow 40e = v_2 - v_1$ ... ②

Adding ① and ②: $40(1 + e) = 2v_2 \Rightarrow v_2 = 20(1 + e)$

For the second collision, the equations are the same, except that 40 is replaced by $20(1 + e)$

$$\Rightarrow \quad 20(1 + e) = v_3 + v_4 \qquad\qquad\qquad \text{... ③}$$
$$20e(1 + e) = v_4 - v_3 \qquad\qquad\qquad \text{... ④}$$

where v_3 and v_4 are the velocities of the last and next-to-last cars in the queue respectively, after their collision.

This gives: $2v_4 = 20(1 + e)^2 \Rightarrow v_4 = 10(1 + e)^2$

You can see from the last equation that the higher the value for e, the greater the speed of the car after collision. In fact, if $e = 1$, the speed after collision is the same as the speed of the colliding car – this is a perfectly elastic collision where no energy is lost. This is the reverse of what the designer requires. With a low value for e, the speed after collision of the car that is hit is only half that of the colliding car, and most of the energy has been absorbed by the crumple zones.

Let's have a look at another example where we use Newton's Experimental Law to find the loss of kinetic energy in a collision.

Example

Two small spheres A and B, having masses $4m$ and $5m$ respectively, move directly towards each other and collide. Immediately before the collision the speeds of A and B are $5u$ and $4u$ respectively. Given that the coefficient of restitution is $\frac{1}{3}$, find the loss of kinetic energy in the collision.

Solution

For the positive direction, we can take A's original direction of motion

Figure 4.3

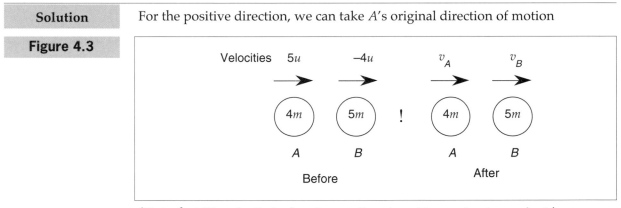

(Note that B's velocity before is **negative** since it's moving **towards** A.)

Conservation of momentum: $(4m)(5u) + (5m)(-4u) = 4mv_A + 5mv_B$ ... ①

(Note that we've assumed that the particles will be moving in a **positive** direction after the collision – if in fact one or both are moving in the opposite direction, their velocities will turn out to be negative when we solve the equations.)

Newton's Experimental Law: $\dfrac{\text{Separation speed}}{\text{Approach speed}} = \dfrac{1}{3} \Rightarrow \dfrac{v_B - v_A}{5u - (-4u)} = \dfrac{1}{3}$ ... ②

We'll now simplify equations ① and ②:

① becomes $20mu - 20mu = 4mv_A + 5mv_B$

$$0 = 4mv_A + 5mv_B$$

Dividing by m and swapping sides,

$$4v_A + 5v_B = 0 \qquad \dots \text{①}$$

② becomes $\dfrac{v_B - v_A}{5u + 4u} = \dfrac{1}{3} \Rightarrow \dfrac{v_B - v_A}{9u} = \dfrac{1}{3}$

$$v_B - v_A = \dfrac{9u}{3} = 3u \qquad \dots \text{②'}$$

Solving ① and ②' simultaneously, we want the coefficients of either v_A or v_B to be the same, so we can multiply ②' by 4 and then have:

$$4v_A + 5v_B = 0 \qquad \dots \text{①''}$$
$$4v_B - 4v_A = 12u \qquad \dots \text{②''}$$

Adding these, $9v_B = 12u$

$$\Rightarrow v_B = \dfrac{12u}{9} = \dfrac{4u}{3} \qquad \dots \text{③}$$

Putting this into ①: $4v_A + 5\left(\dfrac{4u}{3}\right) = 0$

$$4v_A + \dfrac{20u}{3} = 0 \Rightarrow 4v_A = \dfrac{-20u}{3}$$

$$\Rightarrow v_A = \dfrac{-5u}{3} \qquad \dots \text{④}$$

So the velocity of each sphere afterwards has the opposite sign to the velocity before, i.e. they both rebound after the collision.

The kinetic energy is given by $\frac{1}{2}$ mass $\times$ velocity^2 for each particle.

Total kinetic energy before is $\frac{1}{2}(4m)(5u)^2 + \frac{1}{2}(5m)(-4u)^2$

$$= \frac{1}{2} \times 4m \times 25u^2 + \frac{1}{2} \times 5m \times 16u^2$$
$$= 50mu^2 + 40mu^2 = 90mu^2$$

KE after is $\frac{1}{2}(4m)\left(-\dfrac{5u}{3}\right)^2 + \frac{1}{2}(5m)\left(\dfrac{4u}{3}\right)^2$

$$= \frac{1}{2} \times 4m \times \dfrac{25u^2}{9} + \frac{1}{2} \times 5m \times \dfrac{16u^2}{9}$$
$$= \dfrac{50u^2}{9} + \dfrac{40mu^2}{9} = \dfrac{90mu^2}{9} = 10mu^2$$

So the loss of kinetic energy is $90mu^2 - 10mu^2 = 80mu^2$

There will always be a loss of kinetic energy in a simple collision between two particles unless the collision is **perfectly elastic**, i.e. $e = 1$.

Practice questions B

1 Consider the situation shown below:

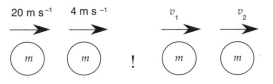

(a) Write down, and simplify, the momentum equation.

(b) If the coefficient of restitution is $\frac{3}{4}$, write down and simplify Newton's Experimental Law.

(c) Deduce the values of v_1 and v_2.

(d) Deduce the loss of kinetic energy as a result of the collision.

2 Consider the situation shown below:

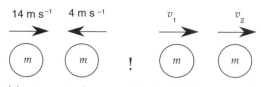

14 m s⁻¹   4 m s⁻¹ v_1 v_2

m m ! m m

(a) Re-write the second ball's initial velocity in an appropriate form.

(b) Write down, and simplify, the momentum equation.

(c) If the coefficient if restitution is $\frac{2}{3}$, write down and simplify Newton's Experimental Law.

(d) Deduce the values of v_1 and v_2.

(e) What is implied by the value of v_1?

(f) Deduce the loss of kinetic energy as a result of the collision.

3 Consider the situation below:

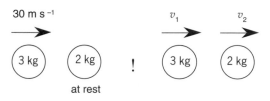

30 m s⁻¹ v_1 v_2

3 kg   2 kg   !   3 kg   2 kg

at rest

(a) Write down, and simplify, the momentum equation.

(b) If the coefficient if restitution is $\frac{5}{6}$, write down and simplify Newton's Experimental Law.

(c) Deduce the values of v_1 and v_2.

(d) Deduce the loss of kinetic energy as a result of the collision.

4 A sphere of mass 6 kg, moving at 4 m s⁻¹, strikes another sphere of mass 4 kg, moving in the same direction with velocity 2 m s⁻¹. If the coefficient of restitution is $\frac{1}{4}$, find:

(a) the velocities after impact

(b) the loss of kinetic energy due to impact.

5 A ball of mass 10 kg, moving at 8 m s⁻¹, impinges directly on a ball of mass 8 kg, moving in the opposite direction at 4 m s⁻¹. If the coefficient of restitution is $\frac{1}{3}$, find:

(a) the velocities after impact

(b) the loss of kinetic energy due to impact.

6 Consider the situation below:

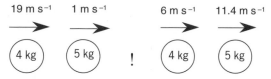

19 m s⁻¹   1 m s⁻¹   6 m s⁻¹   11.4 m s⁻¹

4 kg   5 kg   !   4 kg   5 kg

What is the coefficient of restitution?

7 A smooth sphere of mass 1 kg moving at 7 m s⁻¹ impinges directly on another smooth sphere of mass 2 kg moving in the same direction at 1 m s⁻¹. If the lighter sphere is brought to rest by the impact, find:

(a) the coefficient of restitution

(b) the loss of kinetic energy due to impact.

8 If two particles of equal masses, travelling in opposite directions at equal speeds, collide directly, and if as a result 75 per cent of the kinetic energy is lost, determine the coefficient of restitution.

9 A pebble of mass 0.06 kg skimming across the ice at 10 m s⁻¹ hits a stationary pebble of mass 0.09 kg, which moves off along the same line. If the coefficient of restitution is 0.5, find the speeds after impact. What is the loss of kinetic energy due to impact?

10 A smooth sphere of mass m impinges directly with speed V on another smooth sphere of equal radius, but of mass $2m$, at rest. The motion takes place on a horizontal plane and the coefficient of restitution is $\frac{1}{3}$. Show that the velocities after impact are in the ratio 1:4. After this impact, the heavier sphere impinges directly on a wall. If the coefficient of restitution between the sphere and the wall is $\frac{1}{2}$, show that the impulsive action between them is $\frac{4}{3}mV$.

Multiple collisions

Here is a further example involving more than one collision.

| Example | Three particles A, B and C have masses m, $3m$ and λm respectively. The particles lie at rest on a smooth horizontal plane in a straight line with B between A and C. Particle A is given a horizontal impulse, of magnitude J, and collides directly with B. After this collision A is at rest and B moves towards C with speed u. The coefficient of restitution at each impact is e. |

(a) Find J in terms of m and u.

(b) Show that $e = \frac{1}{3}$.

(c) Find, in terms of m and u, the loss in kinetic energy in the collision between A and B.

Particle B, moving with speed u, collides directly with particle C.

(d) Find, in terms of λ and u, the speeds of B and C after their collision.

(e) Show that A and B will have a second collision provided that $\lambda > 9$.

(f) Given that $\lambda = 6$, find, in terms of m and u, the magnitude of the impulse on B in the collision between B and C.

| Solution | (a) For the initial impulse, |

| Figure 4.4 | |

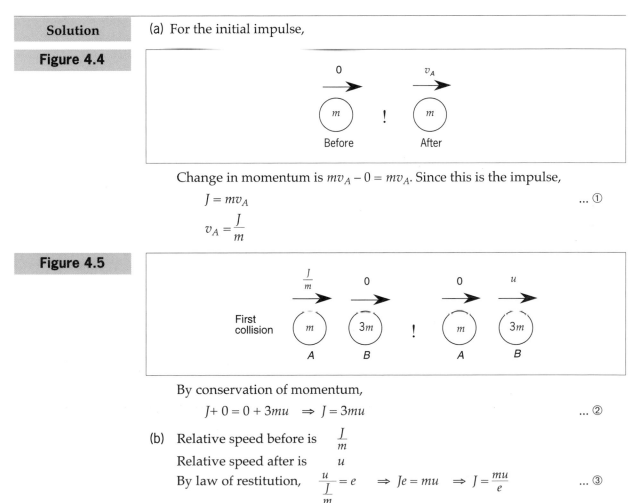

Change in momentum is $mv_A - 0 = mv_A$. Since this is the impulse,

$$J = mv_A \qquad \qquad \text{... ①}$$

$$v_A = \frac{J}{m}$$

| Figure 4.5 | |

By conservation of momentum,

$$J + 0 = 0 + 3mu \quad \Rightarrow \quad J = 3mu \qquad \qquad \text{... ②}$$

(b) Relative speed before is $\dfrac{J}{m}$

Relative speed after is u

By law of restitution, $\dfrac{u}{\frac{J}{m}} = e \quad \Rightarrow \quad Je = mu \quad \Rightarrow \quad J = \dfrac{mu}{e}$ ... ③

Putting ② and ③ together

$$3mu = \frac{mu}{e} \quad \Rightarrow e = \frac{1}{3}$$

(c) Putting ① and ② together

$$mv_A = 3mu$$

so $v_A = 3u$

KE before is $\frac{1}{2} \times m \times (3u)^2 + 0$

KE after is $0 + \frac{1}{2} \times 3m \times u^2$

Loss in KE = KE before – KE after $= \frac{9mu^2}{2} - \frac{3mu^2}{2} = \frac{6mu^2}{2} = 3mu^2$

(d)

Figure 4.6

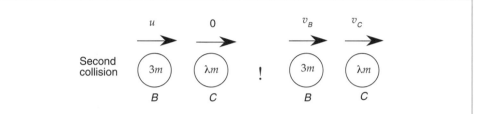

Momentum : $3mu = 3mv_B + \lambda mv_C$

i.e. $3v_B + \lambda v_C = 3u$ ... ④

Restitution : $\dfrac{v_C - v_B}{u} = e = \dfrac{1}{3}$ (answer to part (b))

i.e. $v_C - v_B = \dfrac{u}{3}$ ... ⑤

⑤ × 3 : $3v_C - 3v_B = u$ ... ⑥

④ + ⑥ : $3v_C + \lambda v_C = 4u$

$\Rightarrow \quad (3 + \lambda)v_C = 4u$

$\Rightarrow \quad v_C = \dfrac{4u}{3 + \lambda}$

Putting this into ⑤: $\dfrac{4u}{3 + \lambda} - v_B = \dfrac{u}{3}$

$\therefore \quad v_B = \dfrac{4u}{3 + \lambda} - \dfrac{u}{3} \quad = \dfrac{12u - 3u - \lambda u}{3(3 + \lambda)} = \dfrac{u(9 - \lambda)}{3(3 + \lambda)}$

(e) Since after the first collision between *A* and *B*, *A* is brought to rest, there will be a second collision provided that *B*'s velocity is towards *A* after *B*'s collision with *C*, i.e. provided that $v_B < 0$

i.e. $\dfrac{u(9 - \lambda)}{3(3 + \lambda)} < 0$

We can multiply through by $3(3 + \lambda)$, since this is positive

$$u(9 - \lambda) < 0$$

and divide through by *u*, since this is also positive

$$9 - \lambda < 0 \qquad \Rightarrow \lambda > 9$$

(f) If $\lambda = 6$, $v_C = \frac{4u}{9}$ and the momentum of C after the collision with B is mass × velocity, the impulse of B on C is:

$$\lambda m \times \frac{4u}{9} \qquad \Rightarrow 6m \times \frac{4u}{9} = \frac{8u}{3}$$

This is the impulse of B on C since C was originally at rest, with zero momentum, and impulse is change in momentum. So the impulse of C on B is $\frac{-8u}{3}$ (always equal and opposite) with magnitude $\frac{8u}{3}$ (ignoring the minus sign).

Practice questions C

1 Consider the situation below:

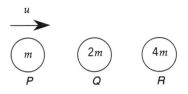

(a) If the coefficient if restitution between P and Q is $\frac{2}{3}$, find the speeds of P and Q after the first impact.

(b) If the coefficient of restitution between Q and R is e, find the speeds of Q and R after the second impact.

(c) If there is a further collision between P and Q, show that $e > 0.8$.

2 Three particles A, B and C of masses $2m$, m and $5m$ kg rest on a smooth horizontal table along the straight line ABC. A is projected towards B with a speed u m s^{-1}. Find the velocities of the particles after the second collision if the coefficient of restitution between each pair of particles is 0.5.

3 Two smooth spheres each of mass 0.5 kg are sliding along a smooth straight groove at the same speed of 2 m s^{-1}, 1 m apart, in the same direction. A third smooth sphere of mass 3 kg sliding along the groove at 3 m s^{-1} in the same direction collides with the second sphere. The coefficient of restitution between any two spheres is 0.75 and all spheres have the same radii.

What time elapses between the first and second impact? Will there be a third impact?

4 Consider the situation below.

If the coefficient if restitution between each pair of spheres is 0.5, prove that there will be just two impacts, and find the speed of each sphere after the second impact.

5 Consider the situation below:

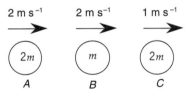

If the coefficient of restitution between B and C is 0.8 and if A and B coalesce on impact, show that in the final motion there are two bodies moving with equal velocities.

6 Three spheres A, B, C of masses $3m$, $2m$, $2m$, and of equal radii, lie on a smooth table with their centres in a straight line. Their coefficient of restitution is 0.25. Show that, if A is projected with velocity u to strike B, there are three impacts, and that the final velocities are $\frac{25}{64}u$, $\frac{57}{128}u$ and $\frac{15}{32}u$.

7 Consider the situation below:

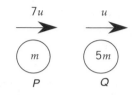

(a) If the coefficient of restitution between the particles is e, find the speeds of P and Q after the collision.

(b) If the direction of motion of P is reversed by the collision, find the range of possible values of e.

8 Consider the situation below:

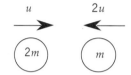

(a) If the coefficient of restitution between the particles is e, find the speeds of each particle after the collision.

(b) Show that the particles move in opposite directions after this collision.

9 Consider the situation below:

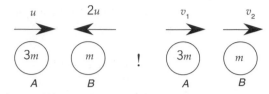

The coefficient of restitution is e.

(a) Find an expression for v_1, in terms of u and e.

(b) Find an expression for v_2 in terms of u and e.

(c) Show that if the direction of motion of A is changed by the collision, then $e > \frac{1}{3}$.

(d) Show that v_2 can never exceed $2.5\,u$.

10 A particle P of mass m, moving with speed u on a smooth horizontal surface, collides directly with a stationery particle Q of mass $2m$. The coefficient of restitution between P and Q is e. The direction of motion of P is reversed by the collision.

(a) Show that the speed of Q after the collision is $\frac{u}{3}(1 + e)$.

(b) Find the speed of P after the collision.

Subsequently, Q hits a fixed wall at right angles to the direction of motion of P and Q. The coefficient of restitution between Q and the wall is $\frac{1}{4}$. After Q rebounds from the wall, there is another collision between P and Q.

(c) Show that $\frac{1}{2} < e < \frac{5}{7}$.

(d) In the case $e = 0.6$, find the magnitude of the impulse exerted on Q by the wall.

SUMMARY EXERCISE

1 Two smooth spheres A and B of equal radii and masses $3m$ and m, respectively, are travelling towards each other along the line of centres. Given that each has speed u and that the collision is perfectly elastic:

(a) show that A is brought to rest by the impact

(b) find the speed of B after the impact.

2 Two spheres A and B, of mass $3m$ and m respectively, are moving towards each other with speeds of $4u$ and u respectively. Find the velocity of each sphere after the collision and show that the loss in kinetic energy is $9mu^2$, given that the coefficient of restitution between the two spheres is $\frac{1}{5}$.

3 Two particles, A and B, of masses $2m$ and $3m$ respectively, are moving in a straight line in the same direction on a smooth horizontal plane. The particles collide and, *after* the collision, A and B continue to move in the same straight line and in the same direction with speeds u and $\frac{3u}{2}$ respectively. Given that the coefficient of restitution between A and B is $\frac{1}{5}$, find, in terms of u, the speed of A and the speed of B *before* their collision. Find also, in terms of m and u, the magnitude of the impulse of the force exerted by B on A during the collision.

4 Three small smooth spheres *A*, *B* and *C*, of masses $15m$, $5m$ and λm, are at rest in a straight line on a horizontal plane. Sphere *A* then moves along the plane and strikes directly sphere *B* which moves off with speed v. Sphere *B* goes on to strike sphere *C* directly. The coefficient of restitution between each pair of spheres is $\frac{1}{2}$.

(a) Find, in terms of v, the speed of *A* before and after impact with *B*.

(b) Find, in terms of m and v the change in:

   (i) the magnitude of the momentum of *A*

   (ii) the magnitude of the momentum of *B*,

   as a result of their collision.

Given that, after the impact of *B* with *C*, there are no further collisions, show that $\lambda \le \frac{40}{19}$.

5 Two small smooth spheres *P* and *Q* of equal radii but of masses m and $3m$ respectively are moving towards each other on a smooth horizontal table. Before collision the speeds of *P* and *Q* are $3u$ and $6u$ respectively and after collision the direction of motion of *P* is reversed and it moves with speed $5u$. Find the impulse on *Q*, the speed of *Q* after the collision and the coefficient of restitution between *P* and *Q*.

After collision, *P* moves with constant speed $5u$ until it catches up, and collides directly, with a third sphere *S* which is identical to *P* and which is moving in the same direction with speed $2u$. The kinetic energy lost in this second collision is $2mu^2$. Find the speed of *P* immediately after colliding with *S*. (The coefficient of restitution between *P* and *S* is not the same as that between *P* and *Q*.)

6 A uniform smooth sphere *A*, of mass m, lies on a smooth horizontal table between a second uniform smooth sphere *B*, of equal size but of mass λm ($\lambda > 0$), and a fixed vertical plane. The line joining the centres of the spheres is normal to the plane. Between both the spheres and between a sphere and the plane the coefficient of restitution is $\frac{3}{5}$. Sphere *A* is projected along the table with speed u towards sphere *B*. Show that the direction of motion of *A* is reversed in the collision provided that $\lambda > \frac{5}{3}$.

Also show that in this case sphere *A*, after rebounding from the vertical plane, will collide again with sphere *B* provided that $\lambda > \frac{55}{9}$.

Given that $\lambda = 15$ show that sphere *A* is reduced to rest after its second collision with *B* and find the final velocity of *B*.

7 The coefficient of restitution between two particles *A* and *B* is e, where $0 < e < 1$. The masses of *A* and *B* are m and em respectively. The particles are moving with constant speeds u and eu in the same horizontal line, and in the same direction, and they collide.

(a) Show that after the collision the speed of *A* is $u(1 - e + e^2)$ and that the speed of *B* is independent of e.

(b) Find the value of e for which the speed of *A* after the collision is least and deduce that, in this case, the total loss of kinetic energy due to the collision is $\frac{1}{32} mu^2$.

(c) Find the possible values of e for which the impulse of the force exerted by *B* on *A* due to the collision has magnitude $\frac{6}{25} mu$.

8 Two small spheres *P* and *Q*, of equal radii and having masses $4m$ and m respectively, are placed at rest on a smooth horizontal plane. The line *PQ* is perpendicular to a fixed vertical barrier with *Q* between *P* and the barrier. The coefficient of restitution between *Q* and the barrier is $\frac{1}{2}$ and between *P* and *Q* is $\frac{2}{3}$.

The sphere *Q* is projected, with speed *U*, directly towards the barrier. Show that the kinetic energy lost when *Q* collides with the barrier is $\frac{3}{8} mU^2$.

Determine how many collisions take place altogether and, for the second collision, find the loss of kinetic energy of the system and find the magnitude of the impulse on *Q*.

9 A ball is thrown vertically upwards with speed *U* from a point halfway between the floor and ceiling of a room of height h. After rebounding from the ceiling and then the floor it just reaches the ceiling a second time. The coefficient of restitution at both floor and ceiling is $\frac{1}{2}$. Denoting the speed of the ball just before its first impact with the floor by *V*, show that $V = \sqrt{(8gh)}$ and find *U* in terms of g and h.

Find the ratio of the magnitude of the impulse when the ball first reaches the ceiling to the magnitude of the impulse on the floor.

SUMMARY

In this section we have deduced from

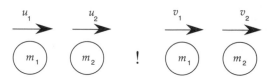

- the momentum equation

$$m_1 u_1 + m_2 u_2 = m_1 v_1 + m_2 v_2$$

- Newton's Experimental Law

$$\frac{v_2 - v_1}{u_1 - u_2} = e, \quad \text{i.e. } v_2 - v_1 = e(u_1 - u_2)$$

We have then:

- solved the above equations simultaneously
- used the fact that $0 \le e \le 1$ to derive inequalities.

We have also:

- considered collisions when three particles are involved
- deduced conditions for further impacts.

ANSWERS

Practice questions A

1 (a) eu (b) eu

2 3.6 m

3 $\dfrac{1}{\sqrt{3}} \sim 0.58$ m

4 5.6 m s^{-1}

5 6.9 m s^{-1} (1 d.p.), 2.43 m

6 0.8

7 2.33 m s^{-1} (2 d.p.)

8 $\sqrt{\dfrac{5}{6}} \sim 0.91$

9 0.5

10 $\sqrt{2 - \sqrt{3}} \sim 0.52$

Practice questions B

1 (a) $24 = v_1 + v_2$ (b) $v_2 - v_1 = 12$
   (c) $v_1 = 6, v_2 = 18$ (d) $28m$ J

2 (a) -4 m s^{-1} (b) $10 = v_1 + v_2$

      $\xrightarrow{}$
      $\bigcirc\!\!\!m$

   (c) $v_2 - v_1 = 12$ (d) $v_1 = -1, v_2 = 11$
   (e) has reversed direction
   (f) $45m$ J

3 (a) $90 = 3v_1 + 2v_2$ (b) $v_2 - v_1 = 25$
   (c) $v_1 = 8, v_2 = 33$ (d) 165 J

4 (a) 3 m s^{-1}, 3.5 m s^{-1} (b) 4.5 J

5 (a) $\dfrac{8}{9}$ m s^{-1}, $4\dfrac{8}{9}$ m s^{-1} (b) $284\dfrac{4}{9}$ J

6 0.3

7 (a) $\frac{3}{4}$ (b) 5.25 J

8 0.5

9 1 m s^{-1}, 6 m s^{-1}, 1.35 J

10 $v_1 = \frac{v}{9}$, $v_2 = \frac{4v}{9}$, etc.

Practice questions C

1 (a) $'P' = \frac{-u}{9}$, $'Q' = \frac{5u}{9}$

    (b) $'Q' = \frac{5u}{27}(1 - 2e)$, $'R' = \frac{5u}{27}(1 + e)$

    (c) $\frac{5u}{27}(2e - 1) > \frac{u}{9} \Rightarrow e > 0.8$

2 $\frac{u}{2}$, $\frac{-u}{4}$, $\frac{u}{4}$

3 $\frac{2}{3}$ seconds, yes

4 8 m s^{-1}, 9 m s^{-1}, 18 m s^{-1}

5 Common velocity of 1.6 m s^{-1}

7 (a) $'P' = (2 - 5e)u$, $'Q' = (2 + e)u$

    (b) $e > 0.4$ ∴ $1 \geq e > 0.4$

8 (a) $-eu$ and $2eu$

    (b) Both directions have changed

9 (a) $\frac{u}{4}(1 - 3e)$ (b) $\frac{u}{4}(1 + 9e)$

    (c) $\frac{u}{4}(1 - 3e) < 0 \Rightarrow 1 - 3e < 0 \Rightarrow \frac{1}{3} < e$

    (d) $e \leq 1$ ∴ $\frac{u}{4}(1 + 9e) \leq \frac{u}{4}(10) = 2.5u$

10 (b) $\frac{u}{3}(2e - 1)$ (d) $\frac{4}{3}mu$

Statics of rigid bodies

INTRODUCTION In Section 5 of Unit M1 we saw how to work out the moment of a force. We then used that idea to solve some equilibrium problems – usually involving see-saws! The one tricky problem that we looked at involved a hinged rod resting across a vertical support. It is questions of this type that we are now going to study in more detail.

Drawing the diagrams

OCR M2 5.8.2

When a rigid body is in equilibrium, the first thing that has to be done is to draw a diagram with all the acting forces clearly shown. And, remember, any normal reaction will be perpendicular to the frictional force or, in the case of a smooth surface, perpendicular to the direction in which the frictional force would have acted.

Example

A ladder, AB, modelled as a uniform rod, rests against a smooth vertical wall, with its base on a rough horizontal floor.

Figure 5.1

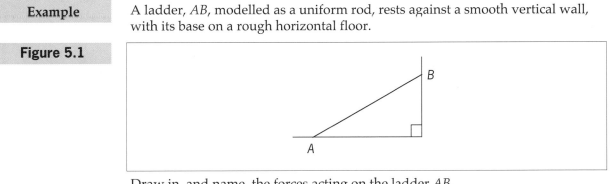

Draw in, and name, the forces acting on the ladder AB.

Solution

This gives the following set-up.

Figure 5.2

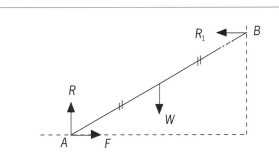

F is the frictional force at A.

R is the normal reaction at A.

R_1 is the normal reaction at B. (There is no frictional force at B.)

W is the weight of the ladder.

65

Example	A non-uniform ladder *AB* rests on a rough sloping ground and across a rough vertical wall.

Figure 5.3	

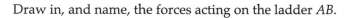

Draw in, and name, the forces acting on the ladder *AB*.

Solution	This gives us the following diagram.

Figure 5.4	

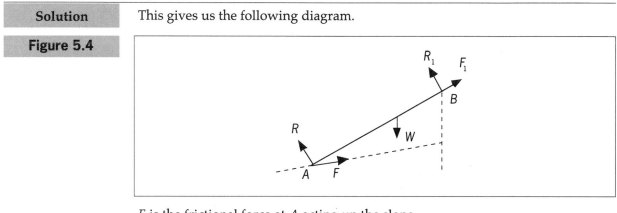

F is the frictional force at *A* acting up the slope.

R is the corresponding normal reaction at *A*.

F_1 is the frictional force at *B*.

R_1 is the corresponding normal reaction at *B*.

W is the weight of the ladder (at the exact midpoint of *AB*).

Practice questions A

1 For each of the following draw in and name the acting forces:

(a)

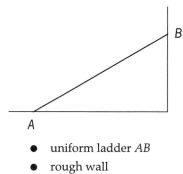

  A

- uniform ladder *AB*
- rough wall
- smooth floor.

(b)

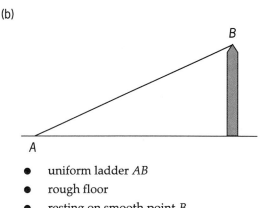

  A

- uniform ladder *AB*
- rough floor
- resting on smooth point *B*.

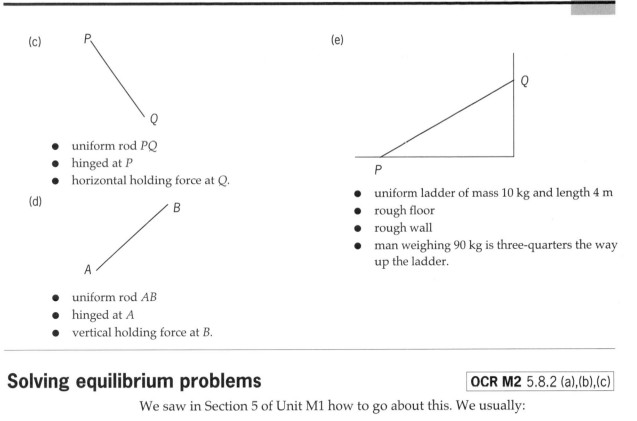

(c)

- uniform rod PQ
- hinged at P
- horizontal holding force at Q.

(d)

- uniform rod AB
- hinged at A
- vertical holding force at B.

(e)

- uniform ladder of mass 10 kg and length 4 m
- rough floor
- rough wall
- man weighing 90 kg is three-quarters the way up the ladder.

Solving equilibrium problems

OCR M2 5.8.2 (a),(b),(c)

We saw in Section 5 of Unit M1 how to go about this. We usually:

- resolve vertically and get zero
- resolve horizontally and get zero
- take moments about any point and get zero.

And, of course, we need that clear diagram!

Example

A uniform ladder of mass 20 kg and length 4 m rests on a rough horizontal floor and against a smooth vertical wall. The ladder makes an angle of 30° with the floor. If the coefficient of friction between the floor and the ladder is μ, comment on the stability of the system in the following cases:

(a) $\mu = 0.9$ (b) $\mu = 0.8$

For what value of μ is the ladder in limiting equilibrium?

Solution

First we need that clear force diagram, as in Fig. 5.5.

Figure 5.5

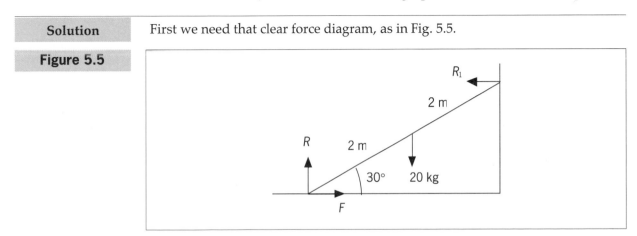

- *F* is the required frictional force at the base.
- *R* is the corresponding normal reaction.
- R_1 is the normal reaction from the smooth wall.

Resolving ↑ : $R = 20g$ ... ①

Resolving → : $F = R_1$ ... ②

base ↺ : $20g \times 2 \cos 30° = R_1 \times 4 \sin 30°$ ... ③

We can therefore find the forces *F*, *R* and R_1 that are necessary to keep the ladder in equilibrium.

      Equation ③ gives $R_1 = 169.7$ N (1 d.p.)

∴   Equation ② gives $F = 169.7$ N (1 d.p.)

and Equation ① gives $R = 196$ N

In case (a), $\mu = 0.9$

∴ The maximum frictional force available $= \mu R$

                                           $= 0.9 \times 196 = 176.4$ N

But we only need *F* to be 169.7 N for equilibrium.

∴ In case (a), the ladder is stable.

In case (b), $\mu = 0.8$

∴ The maximum frictional force available $= \mu R$

                                           $= 0.8 \times 196 = 156.8$ N

But we need *F* to be 169.7 N for equilibrium

∴ In case (b), the ladder slides to the ground.

Limiting equilibrium occurs when $F = \mu R$

∴ $169.7 = \mu \times 196$

∴ $\mu = 0.866$

∴ The ladder is stable provided $\mu \geq 0.866$.

Example

A uniform rod *AB* of length 0.8 m and mass 2.8 kg, is smoothly hinged at *A* to a fixed vertical wall. The rod is held in equilibrium by a horizontal force of magnitude *F* newtons, acting at *B* in the vertical plane containing *AB*. The rod makes an angle of 40° with the wall.

Figure 5.6

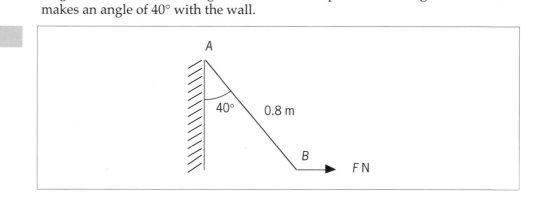

Find:

(a) the value of F

(b) the horizontal and vertical components of the force on the rod at A, indicating clearly the directions in which the components act.

Solution	First we need that clear diagram:
Figure 5.7	

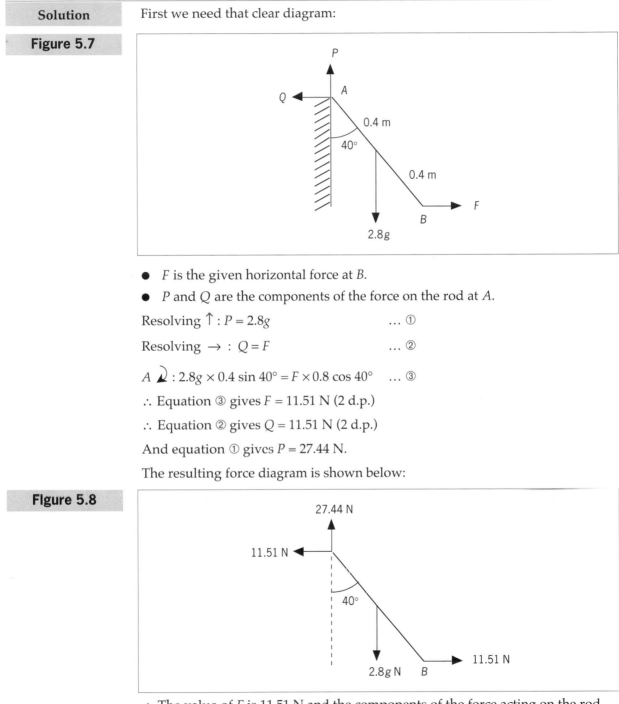

- F is the given horizontal force at B.
- P and Q are the components of the force on the rod at A.

Resolving $\uparrow$: $P = 2.8g$ ... ①

Resolving $\rightarrow$: $Q = F$ ... ②

$A \curvearrowright$: $2.8g \times 0.4 \sin 40° = F \times 0.8 \cos 40°$ ... ③

$\therefore$ Equation ③ gives $F = 11.51$ N (2 d.p.)

$\therefore$ Equation ② gives $Q = 11.51$ N (2 d.p.)

And equation ① gives $P = 27.44$ N.

The resulting force diagram is shown below:

Figure 5.8

$\therefore$ The value of F is 11.51 N and the components of the force acting on the rod at A are shown in the diagram above.

Practice questions B

1 *AB* is a non uniform rod of mass 50 kg and length 0.8 m. Find the forces *T*, *P* and *Q* if the rod is in equilibrium.

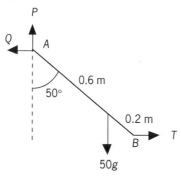

2 *AB* is a uniform rod of mass 50 kg and length 1 m. Find the forces *T*, *P* and *Q* if the rod is in equilibrium.

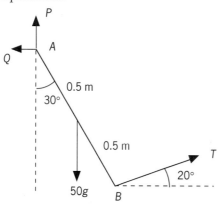

3 A uniform ladder of mass 80 kg, length 4 m, leans against a smooth vertical wall. The angle of inclination is 50°.

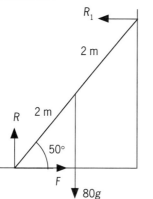

Find forces *F*, *R* and R_1 if the system is in equilibrium.

4 A uniform ladder of mass 90 kg, length 4 m, leans against a rough vertical wall but is resting on a smooth horizontal floor. The angle of inclination is 44°.

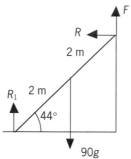

Find forces *F*, *R* and R_1 if the system is in equilibrium.

5 A uniform ladder of mass 85 kg, length 4 m, leans against a smooth vertical wall. The angle of inclination is 35°.

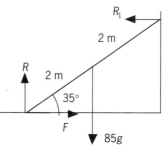

Find the forces, *F*, *R* and R_1 if the system is in equilibrium.

If the system is in limiting equilibrium, find the coefficient of friction μ.

6 A uniform rod *AB* of mass 30 kg and length 4 m leans across a smooth vertical support. The top of the support is 2.4 m from *A* and *AB* makes an angle of 50° with the horizontal.

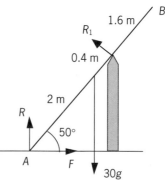

Find the forces F, R and R_1 if the system is in equilibrium.

If the system is in limiting equilibrium, find the coefficient of friction between the rod and the ground.

7 A uniform rod AB of weight 50 N is freely hinged at A. The rod is in equilibrium at an angle α to the horizontal when a horizontal force 25 N acts at B. Calculate α and the reaction of the hinge on the rod in magnitude and direction.

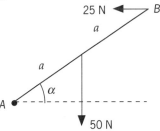

8 A uniform rod AB of weight 60 N is freely hinged at A. The rod is held at an angle α to the horizontal by a force of 15 N at B acting perpendicular to the rod. Calculate α and the reaction of the hinge on the rod.

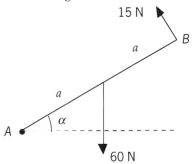

9 A uniform rod AB of weight 50 N is pivoted at A and held in a horizontal position by a light string attached to B and to a point vertically above A. The string is inclined at 30° to the horizontal. Calculate the tension in the string and the reaction of the rod on the pivot at A.

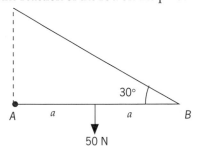

10 A uniform ladder AB of weight 250 N rests at an angle of 30° to a smooth vertical wall with the end B on rough horizontal ground. Find the reaction of the wall on the ladder and the least value of the coefficient of friction at B.

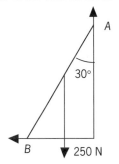

11 A uniform ladder AB of weight 150 N and length 13 m rests with the end A against a smooth vertical wall and the end B on rough horizontal ground. The foot of the ladder is 5 m from the wall. Calculate the reaction of the wall on the ladder, the total reaction of the ground on the ladder and the least value of the coefficient of friction at B.

12 A uniform ladder of weight 100 N rests with one end on rough ground and the other end against a rough vertical wall. The coefficients of friction at the ground and at the wall are $\frac{1}{2}$ and $\frac{1}{3}$ respectively. If the ladder is in limiting equilibrium, find the inclination of the ladder to the horizontal.

13 A uniform beam AB of weight 100 N can turn in a vertical plane about a hinge at A, and to the other end B is tied a rope which passes over a smooth pulley C, vertically above A, so that $AC = AB$. Find the tension in the rope necessary to keep the beam at an angle of 60° with the horizontal. Find also the direction and magnitude of the reaction at the hinge.

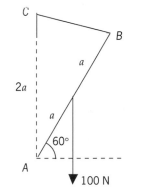

14 A uniform rod 3 m long is suspended by a light string of length 5 m passing over a smooth peg, and rests horizontally, the string being attached to the ends of the rod. If the rod has mass 7 kg, find the tension in the string.

15 A uniform rod AB of mass 10 kg is smoothly hinged at A and rests in a vertical plane with the end B against a smooth vertical wall. If the rod makes an angle of 40° with the wall, find the pressure on the wall and the magnitude and direction of the reaction at A.

16 A uniform ladder 12.5 m long, and of mass 60 kg, rests with its top against a smooth vertical wall and its foot on rough ground 3.5 m from the wall. Find the normal and friction forces at the bottom of the ladder.

17 The foot of a uniform 30 kg ladder is on rough horizontal ground and its top rests against a smooth vertical wall. The ladder makes 60° with the horizontal and is in limiting equilibrium. Find the coefficient of friction between the ground and the wall, correct to 2 d.p. If a 60 kg man stands three quarters of the way up the ladder, what horizontal force applied to the foot of the ladder is needed to keep it in equilibrium?

18 A uniform ladder rests with an end against a smooth vertical wall and the other end on a rough horizontal floor. The coefficient of friction between the floor and the ladder is $\frac{5}{18}\sqrt{3}$. The inclination of the ladder to the horizontal is 60°. Show that a girl whose weight is twice the weight of the ladder can just get to the top without the ladder slipping.

19 A uniform rectangular door, 2 m by 0.8 m, weighs 16 kg. It is in a vertical plane with its longer edges vertical and can turn freely about two hinges attached to one end of its longer edges. The hinges are 0.2 m from either end. Find the horizontal components of the reactions at the hinges. If the door is fitted badly so that the whole weight of the door is carried by the upper hinge A, find the resultant reaction at A.

20 A uniform beam AB 6 m long is free to turn in a vertical plane about a hinge at A. The beam has mass 200 kg and carries a load of mass 300 kg at B. It is supported with AB horizontal by a light rope attached to a point of the beam 2 m from B and to a point 3 m vertically above A. Find the tension in the rope and the reaction at the hinge.

SUMMARY EXERCISE

1

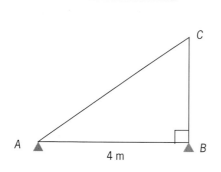

A uniform plate ABC has mass 80 kg. The triangle ABC is right angled at B and $AB = 4$ m. The plate is vertical and rests on two horizontal supports at A and B.

(a) Write down the horizontal distance of the centre of mass of the plate from A.

(b) Find the magnitude of the forces on the supports at A and B.

2

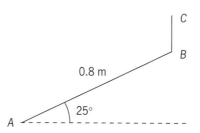

A uniform rod AB has mass 1.6 kg and length 0.8 m. The end A of the rod is pivoted at a fixed point. A light inextensible string has one end attached to B and the other end attached to a fixed point C. The point C is in the same vertical plane as AB and is such that BC is vertical. The rod is in equilibrium, inclined at 25° to the horizontal with B higher than A. Find:

(a) the tension in the string

(b) the horizontal and vertical components of the force acting on the rod at A.

3

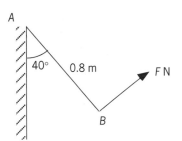

A uniform rod AB of length 0.8 m and mass 4 kg, is smoothly hinged at A to a fixed vertical wall. The rod is held in equilibrium by a force of magnitude F newtons, acting at B in the vertical plane containing AB. The direction of F makes an angle of 90° with the rod AB and the rod makes an angle of 40° with the wall. Find:

(a) the value of F

(b) the horizontal and vertical components of the force on the rod at A, indicating clearly the directions in which the components act.

4

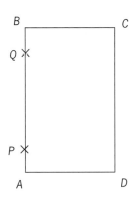

An open rectangular door $ABCD$ is smoothly hinged at the points P and Q of the vertical edge AB.

$AB = 2$ m, $BC = 0.8$ m, $AP = BQ = 0.3$ m and the weight of the door is 150 N.

(a) By modelling the door as a uniform lamina, find the horizontal components of the forces on the door at P and Q.

A wedge is placed between the door and the floor at D, exerting a vertically upward force of magnitude F newtons on the door.

(b) Given that the horizontal components of the forces on the door at P and Q are now both zero, calculate F.

5

A ladder of mass 12 kg making an angle of 65° with the horizontal leans against a smooth vertical wall. A man whose mass is 60 kg stands on the ladder at a point three quarters of the way up. By modelling the ladder as a uniform rod and the man as a particle, find:

(a) the magnitude and direction of the contact force exerted on the ladder by the wall

(b) the horizontal and vertical components on the contact force exerted on the ladder by the ground.

SUMMARY   In this section we have:

- drawn clear diagrams to show the forces acting on rigid bodies in equilibrium

- solved equilibrium problems by:

    (a) resolving horizontally and getting zero

    (b) resolving vertically and getting zero

    (c) taking moments about any point and getting zero.

ANSWERS

Practice questions A

1 (a)

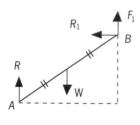

(b)

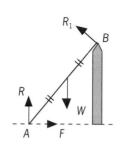

(Normal reaction R_1 at right angles to the rod)

(c)

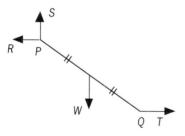

W is the weight.

T is the holding force.

R and *S* are the components of the force at the hinge.

(d)

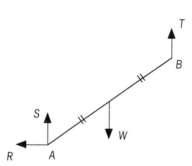

T is the holding force.

W is the weight.

R and *S* are the components of the force at the hinge. (In fact, *R* = 0 — as seen by resolving.)

(e)

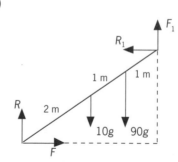

Practice questions B

1 $T \sim 438$ N, $Q \sim 438$ N, $P = 490$ N

2 $T \sim 124$ N, $Q \sim 117$ N, $P \sim 447$ N

3 $F \sim 329$ N, $R_1 \sim 329$ N, $R = 784$ N

4 $F \sim 441$ N, $R = 0$, $R_1 = 441$ N

5 $F \sim 595$ N, $R = 833$ N, $R_1 \sim 595$ N, $\mu = 0.71$ (2 d.p.)

6 $F \sim 121$ N, $R \sim 193$ N, $R_1 \sim 157$ N, $\mu = 0.63$ (2 d.p.)

7 $\alpha = 45°$

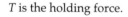

$\therefore \sim 55.9$ N at $\sim 63.4°$ to horizontal

8 $60°$, ~ 54 N at $\sim 76.1°$ to horizontal

9 50 N, 50N at 30° to horizontal

10 ~ 72.2 N, 0.29 (2 d.p.)

11 31.25 N, ~ 153 N at $\sim 78°$ horizontal, 0.21 (2 d.p.)

12 $\sim 39.8°$

13 ~ 25.9 N, ~ 96.6 N at 75° horizontal

14 $4.375g = 42\frac{7}{8}$ N

15 ~ 41.1 N, ~ 106.3 N at $\sim 67.2°$ to horizontal

16 588 N, 85.75 N

17 0.29 (2 d.p.), ~ 83.7 N

19 Each one is 39.2 N, ~ 161.6 N at $\sim 76°$ to horizontal

20 9800 N, ~ 7901 N at $\sim 7.1°$ to *AB*.

M2
Practice examination paper

(Take g = 9.8 m s^{-2} whenever necessary)

1

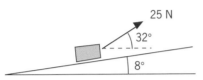

A crate of mass 6 kg is pulled directly up a rough slope, of inclination 8°, by a constant force of magnitude 25 N, acting at an angle of 32° above the horizontal. Find the work done by the force as the crate moves a distance of 4 m up the slope. Find also the work done against gravity in the displacement.

2

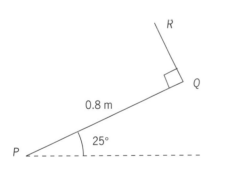

A uniform rod PQ has mass 1.5 kg and length 0.8 m. The end P of the rod is pivoted at a fixed point. A light inextensible string has one end attached to Q and the other end attached to a fixed point R. The point R is in the same vertical plane as PQ and is such angle PQR is 90°. The rod is in equilibrium, inclined at 25° to the horizontal with Q higher than P. Calculate:

(a) the tension in the string

(b) the horizontal and vertical components of the force acting on the rod at P.

3 A particle P of mass 0.2 kg moves so that, at time t seconds, the acceleration $\mathbf{a}$ m s^{-2} is given by

$$\mathbf{a} = 4t\mathbf{i} + 8\sqrt{t}\,\mathbf{j}, \quad (t > 0)$$

where the unit vectors $\mathbf{i}$ and $\mathbf{j}$ are directed due east and north respectively.

(a) When $t = 4$, find the magnitude of the resultant force acting on P.

Given that the velocity of P at $t = 0$ is $5\mathbf{j}$ m s^{-1}, find:

(b) an expression for the velocity of P in terms of t

(c) the direction of motion of P when $t = 4$, giving you answer as a bearing to the nearest degree.

4 At time t seconds, a particle P has position vector, $\mathbf{r}$ metres, relative to a point O given by

$$\mathbf{r} = 5t^2\mathbf{i} + \tfrac{2}{7}t^{3.5}\mathbf{j}$$

At the instant $t = 4$,

(a) show that the particle is moving with velocity $(40\mathbf{i} + 32\mathbf{j})$ m s^{-1}

(b) find the magnitude of the acceleration of the particle

5

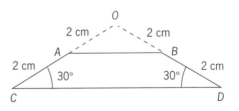

A thin uniform lamina $ABCD$ is formed by taking an isosceles triangle OCD, with two equal sides of 4 cm and base angles of 30°, and removing triangle OAB, where A and B are the midpoints of OC and OD respectively.

(a) Find the distance of the centre of mass of the lamina from CD.

The lamina is freely suspended from A and hangs at rest in a vertical plane.

(b) Find, to the nearest degree, the acute angle between AB and the vertical.

6 A man throws a ball from the top of a vertical cliff 18 m high. It is observed that the ball rises to a height of 8 m above the top of the cliff before falling, and that it strikes the sea at a distance 36 m from the base of the cliff. By modelling the ball as a particle, and assuming no air resistance, find:

(a) the vertical component of the velocity of projection

(b) the time of flight

(c) the horizontal component of the velocity of projection

(d) the direction of flight of the ball as it strikes the sea.

7 A car of mass 1800 kg is towing a caravan of mass 600 kg, by means of a light inextensible towbar, up a straight road which is inclined at an angle α to the horizontal where $\sin\alpha = 0.2$. The towbar is parallel to the road. The car's engine is working at a constant rate of 90 kW. The resistances to motion due to non-gravitational forces are constant, having magnitude 1100 N for the car and 450 N for the caravan.

At a given instant, the car and caravan are both moving with a speed of 8 m s^{-1}. Find:

(a) the magnitude of the acceleration of the caravan

(b) the tension in the towbar.

At this instant the towbar breaks.

(c) Find the further distance moved by the caravan before it comes momentarily to rest.

8 A particle P of mass m is at rest on smooth horizontal ground at a distance 2 m from a vertical wall. Another particle Q, also of mass m, is moving with speed u in a straight line along the ground towards the wall in a direction which is perpendicular to the wall. Particle Q strikes particle P directly. The coefficient of restitution between P and Q is $\frac{1}{3}$.

(a) Show that the speeds of P and Q after the collision are $\frac{2u}{3}$ and $\frac{u}{3}$ respectively.

Particle P then goes on to strike the wall. The coefficient of restitution between P and the wall is also $\frac{1}{3}$.

(b) Show that P and Q collide for a second time at a distance 0.4 m from the wall.

M2

Solutions

Section 1

1 To reach the window

$\downarrow:$
u	v	a	s	t
0		9.8	?	0.8

$\therefore s = ut + \frac{1}{2}at^2 \Rightarrow s = 3.136$

$\therefore$ Required height $= 3.136 + 3 = 6.136$ m

2 Consider the ball as being projected downwards with a speed of -40 m s^{-1}

$\therefore \downarrow:$
u	v	a	s	t
-40		9.8	75	?

$\therefore s = ut + \frac{1}{2}at^2 \quad \Rightarrow 75 = -40t + 4.9t^2$

$\Rightarrow 4.9t^2 - 40t - 75 = 0$

Solve this quadratic and get $t = 9.735$
(Ignore the other solution of -1.572 seconds.)

$\therefore$ Required time $= 9.735$ seconds.

3 From the deck onwards

$\downarrow:$
u	v	a	s	t
		9.8	8	0.5

$\therefore s = ut + \frac{1}{2}at^2 \Rightarrow 8 = 0.5u + 1.225 \Rightarrow u = 13.55$

$\therefore$ Block reaches the deck with a speed of 13.55 m s^{-1}

$\therefore$ From the mast-head to the deck:

$\downarrow:$
u	v	a	s	t
0	13.55	9.8	?	

$\therefore v^2 = u^2 + 2as \Rightarrow 13.55^2 = 19.6s \Rightarrow s = 9.37$

$\therefore$ Height above the deck $= 9.37$ m.

4

43.3 m s^{-1} / 25 m s^{-1}

(a) $\uparrow: 0 = 43.3 - 9.8t \Rightarrow t = 4.42$ seconds

$\therefore$ time of flight $= 2 \times 4.42 = 8.84$ seconds

(b) $\rightarrow:$ range $= 25 \times 8.84 = 220.9$ m

(c) $\uparrow: s = \frac{43.3}{2} \times 4.42 = 95.7$ m

(d) $\uparrow: s = 43.3 \times 2 - 4.9 \times 4 = 67$ m

(e) $\uparrow v = 43.3 - 9.8 \times 3 = 13.9$

13.9 m s^{-1} / 25 m s^{-1} / α

$\therefore \alpha = 29°$ to horizontal

5

25 ms^{-1} / 43.3 m s^{-1}

(a) $\uparrow: 0 = 25 - 9.8t \therefore t = 2.55$

$\therefore s = \frac{25}{2} \times 2.55 = 31.89$ m

$\therefore$ Greatest height $= 131.89$ m.

(b) $\downarrow: 131.89 = 4.9t^2 \therefore t = 5.188$ seconds

$\therefore$ Time of flight $= 2.55 + 5.188 = 7.74$ seconds

(c) $\rightarrow:$ range $= 43.3 \times 7.74 = 335$ m

(d) $\downarrow v = 9.8 \times 5.188 = 50.84$

50.84 m s^{-1} / v / α / 43.3 m s^{-1}

$\therefore \quad v = 66.8$ m s^{-1}

and $\quad \alpha = 49.6°$ to horizontal

6 (a) $\downarrow: 100 = 4.9t^2 \qquad \therefore 100 = 4.9t^2$
$\therefore t = 4.52$ seconds

(b) $\rightarrow:$ range $= 60 \times 4.52 = 271$ m

(c) $\downarrow: s = 0 + \frac{1}{2} \times 9.8 \times 4 = 19.6$ m

$\therefore 80.4$ m above the sea

(d) $\downarrow v = 9.8 \times 3 = 29.4$

29.4 m s^{-1} / v / α / 60 m s^{-1}

$\therefore \alpha = 26\cdot1°$ to horizontal

(e) $v = 66.82$ m s^{-1}

7 (a) $\uparrow$: $15 = 20t - 4.9t^2$

∴ $t = 0.99$ seconds or 3.09 (quadratic)

∴ Takes 0.99 seconds to reach P

(b) 3.09 seconds is the time to go up to Q and then fall back to P

∴ Time from P to $Q = \dfrac{3.09 - 0.99}{2} = 1.05$ seconds

(c) Time taken to reach Q is $0.99 + 1.05 = 2.04$ seconds

∴ $\uparrow$: $s = \left(\dfrac{20 + 0}{2}\right) 2.04 = 20.4$ m.

∴ $PQ = 20.4 - 15 = 5.4$ m

(d) $3.09 - 0.99 = 2.1$ seconds (see (b))

8 $\uparrow$: $0 = 25 - 9.8t$ ∴ $t = 2.55$ seconds to reach maximum height

∴ Time of flight $= 2 \times 2.55 = 5.1$ seconds

$\rightarrow$: $s = 15 \times 5.1 = 76.5$ m

9 (a)

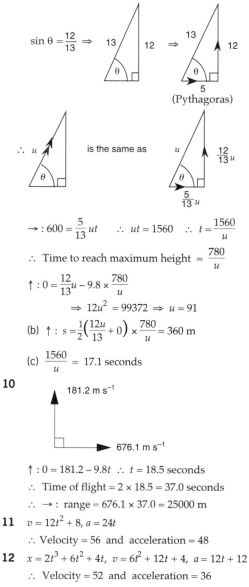

$\sin\theta = \dfrac{12}{13}$ ⇒   13   12   ⇒   13   12

5 (Pythagoras)

∴ u is the same as u $\dfrac{12}{13}u$

$\dfrac{5}{13}u$

$\rightarrow$: $600 = \dfrac{5}{13}ut$ ∴ $ut = 1560$ ∴ $t = \dfrac{1560}{u}$

∴ Time to reach maximum height $= \dfrac{780}{u}$

$\uparrow$: $0 = \dfrac{12}{13}u - 9.8 \times \dfrac{780}{u}$

⇒ $12u^2 = 99372$ ⇒ $u = 91$

(b) $\uparrow$: $s = \dfrac{1}{2}\left(\dfrac{12u}{13} + 0\right) \times \dfrac{780}{u} = 360$ m

(c) $\dfrac{1560}{u} = 17.1$ seconds

10

181.2 m s^{-1}

676.1 m s^{-1}

$\uparrow$: $0 = 181.2 - 9.8t$ ∴ $t = 18.5$ seconds

∴ Time of flight $= 2 \times 18.5 = 37.0$ seconds

∴ $\rightarrow$: range $= 676.1 \times 37.0 = 25000$ m

11 $v = 12t^2 + 8$, $a = 24t$

∴ Velocity $= 56$ and acceleration $= 48$

12 $x = 2t^3 + 6t^2 + 4t$, $v = 6t^2 + 12t + 4$, $a = 12t + 12$

∴ Velocity $= 52$ and acceleration $= 36$

13 $v = 2t + 1$ ⇒ $v = 7$ m s^{-1}

$2t + 1 = 9$ ⇒ $t = 4$ seconds

14 $v = 4t^3 + c$ but $v = 6$ when $t = 1$ ∴ $v = 4t^3 + 2$

∴ $t = 0$ ⇒ $v = 2$ m s^{-1}.

$4t^3 + 2 = 500$ ⇒ $t^3 = 124.5$ ⇒ $t = 4.99$ seconds

15 $\dfrac{dv}{dt} = 6t - t^2 = 0$ ⇒ $t = 0$ or 6

$x = t^3 - \dfrac{1}{12}t^4 + 9t + c$

∴ $t = 0$ ⇒ $x = c$ and $t = 6$ ⇒ $x = 162 + c$

∴ Distance covered $= 162$ m

16 $v = 0$ when $t = 0$ or 1 minute

$v = \dfrac{4}{3}t - \dfrac{4}{3}t^2$, $x = \dfrac{2}{3}t^2 - \dfrac{4}{9}t^3$

(a) $t = 1$ ⇒ $x = \dfrac{2}{9}$

∴ Average velocity $= \dfrac{2}{9}$ km/min $= 13\dfrac{1}{3}$ km/h

(b) Maximum velocity when acceleration is zero

∴ $\dfrac{4}{3} - \dfrac{8}{3}t = 0$ ⇒ $t = 0.5$ minute

⇒ $v = \dfrac{1}{3}$ km/min $= 20$ km/h

17 (a) $x = t + 2t^2 + 2t^3 - 5$ (when $t = 1$, $x = 0$)

∴ $t = 3$ ⇒ $x = 70$

⇒ average velocity $= \dfrac{70}{2} = 35$ m s^{-1}

(b) $t = 1$, $v = 11$ and $t = 3$, $v = 67$

⇒ average acceleration $= \dfrac{67 - 11}{2} = 28$ m s^{-2}

18 $v = kt - \dfrac{1}{12}t^2$ (when $t = 0$, $v = 0$)

∴ $v = 60$, $t = 60$ ⇒ $60 = 60k - 300$ ⇒ $k = 6$

∴ $v = 6t - \dfrac{1}{12}t^2$ ⇒ $x = 3t^2 - \dfrac{1}{36}t^3$

(when $t = 0$, $x = 0$)

∴ $t = 60$ ⇒ $x = 4800$ m

19 $v = 12t^2 - 4t^3$ ($v = 0$, $t = 0$),

$x = 4t^3 - t^4$ ($x = 0$, $t = 0$)

(a) $x = 0$ ⇒ $t = 4$ s ⇒ $v = -64$ m s^{-1}

(b) maximum x when $v = 0$ ⇒ $t = 3$

⇒ $x = 27$ m

(c) maximum velocity when acceleration is zero

⇒ $24t - 12t^2 = 0$ ⇒ $t = 2$ ⇒ $v = 16$ m s^{-1}

However greatest speed when $t = 4$ ∴ 64 m s^{-1}

20 (a) $v = 0$ ⇒ $t = -\dfrac{1}{2}$ or $1\dfrac{1}{2}$ (quadratic)

∴ P at $11.59\dfrac{1}{2}$ a.m, and Q at $12.01\dfrac{1}{2}$ p.m.

(b) $x = \dfrac{3}{8}t + \dfrac{1}{4}t^2 - \dfrac{1}{6}t^3 + \dfrac{5}{48}$ ($x = 0$ when $t = -\dfrac{1}{2}$)

(c) $t = 1\dfrac{1}{2}$ ⇒ $x = \dfrac{2}{3}$ ⇒ average velocity $= \dfrac{2}{3} \div 2$

$= \dfrac{1}{3}$ km/min $= 20$ km/h

(d) Acceleration $= 0$ ⇒ $t = \dfrac{1}{2}$ ⇒ maximum velocity

$= \dfrac{1}{2}$ km/min $= 30$ km/h

21

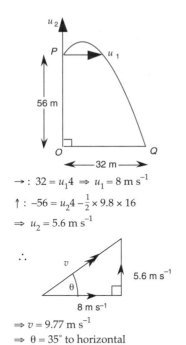

$\rightarrow$: $32 = u_1 4 \Rightarrow u_1 = 8 \text{ m s}^{-1}$

$\uparrow$: $-56 = u_2 4 - \frac{1}{2} \times 9.8 \times 16$

$\Rightarrow u_2 = 5.6 \text{ m s}^{-1}$

$\therefore$

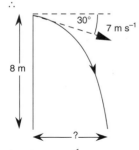

$\Rightarrow v = 9.77 \text{ m s}^{-1}$

$\Rightarrow \theta = 35°$ to horizontal

22 $F = ma$ down the roof $\Rightarrow mg \sin 30° = ma$

$\Rightarrow a = 4.9 \text{ m s}^{-2}$

Leaves roof with velocity v where

$v^2 = u^2 + 2 \times 4.9 \times 5 \Rightarrow v = 7 \text{ m s}^{-1}$

$\therefore$

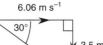

Resolve 7 m s^{-1} to get

$\therefore \downarrow$: $8 = 3.5t + \frac{1}{2} \times 9.8 \times t^2 \Rightarrow t = 0.97$ seconds
(quadratic)

$\therefore \rightarrow$: range $= 6.06 \times 0.97 = 5.88 \text{ m}$

23 (a) $v_1 = \frac{t^2}{10}$ (no +c because starts from rest)

$\therefore t = 5 \Rightarrow v_1 = 2.5 \text{ m/s}$

(b) $v_2 = \frac{t^2}{10} - \frac{10}{t} + 2$

$\left(\int \frac{10}{t^2}dt = \int 10t^{-2}\,dt = -10t^{-1} = -\frac{10}{t}.\right.$

Also $v_2 = 5$ when $t = 5\Big)$

$\therefore t = 10 \Rightarrow v_2 = 11 \text{ m/s}$

24 (a) $a = 6t + 2 \therefore t = 2 \Rightarrow a = 14 \text{ m s}^{-2}$

(b) $x = t^3 + t^2 + c$

$\therefore t = 3, x = 36 + c$ and $t = 4, x = 80 + c$

$\Rightarrow$ distance covered $= 44 \text{ m}$

25 (a) $a = k(7 - t^2)$

$\therefore v = k\left(7t - \frac{t^3}{3}\right) (t = 0$ when $v\ 0)$

But $t = 3$ when $v = 6 \therefore k = \frac{1}{2}$

$\therefore v = \frac{1}{2}\left(7t - \frac{t^3}{3}\right)$

$\therefore s = \frac{1}{2}\left(\frac{7t^2}{2} - \frac{t^4}{12}\right) t = 0$ when $s = 0)$

$\therefore s = \frac{t^2}{24}(42 - t^2)$

(b) $v = 0 \Rightarrow t = \sqrt{21} \Rightarrow s = 18.375 \text{ m}.$

26 (a) $\downarrow : 3\frac{4}{15} = -49 \sin \alpha t + 4.9t^2$

$\rightarrow : 98 = 49 \cos \alpha t$

Eliminate t and get

$3\frac{4}{15} = -98 \tan \alpha + 19.6 \sec^2\alpha$

$\therefore 3\frac{4}{15} = -98 \tan \alpha + 19.6 (1 + \tan^2\alpha)$

$\therefore 19.6 \tan^2\alpha - 98 \tan \alpha + 16\frac{1}{3} = 0$

$\therefore 6 \tan^2\alpha - 30 \tan \alpha + 5 = 0$

(b) Quadratic gives

$\tan \alpha = 4.83$ or $0.17 \Rightarrow \alpha = 78°$ or $10°$

(c) $\alpha = 78° \Rightarrow t = 10$ seconds and
$\alpha = 10° \Rightarrow t = 2$ seconds

$\therefore$ 2 seconds is smallest time.

27 $t = 0, \mathbf{r} = -3\mathbf{i} + 12\mathbf{j}$; $t = 1, \mathbf{r} = 8\mathbf{j}$

$t = 2, \mathbf{r} = 3\mathbf{i} + 4\mathbf{j}$; $t = 3, \mathbf{r} = 6\mathbf{i}$

$t = 4, \mathbf{r} = 9\mathbf{i} - 4\mathbf{j}.$

(a) The path is shown in the following diagram.

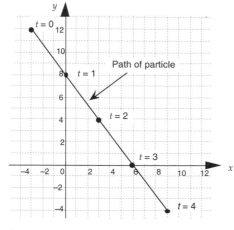

(b) The particle is closest to the origin when the magnitude of:

$\mathbf{r} = (3t - 3)\mathbf{i} + (12 - 4t)\mathbf{j}$ is least.

This is equivalent to finding the minimum value of:

$(3t - 3)^2 + (12 - 4t)^2$

Simplify the brackets to get $25t^2 - 114t + 153$

Now differentiate and put equal to zero

$\therefore\ 50t - 114 = 0 \Rightarrow t = 2.28$

(c) Looking at the diagram, this certainly seems reasonable – the particle is closest somewhere between $t = 2$ and $t = 3$.

Finally $t = 2.28 \Rightarrow \mathbf{r} = 3.84\mathbf{i} + 2.88\mathbf{i}$

The magnitude of $\mathbf{r} = \sqrt{3.84^2 + 2.88^2} = 4.8$ cm
(Alternatively you could drop a perpendicular from the origin to the line $3y + 4x = 24$, solve simultaneously and get $x = 3.84$, $y = 2.88$. Then substitute back and get $t = 2.28$)

An important example: give it some thought.

28 (a) $\dot{\mathbf{r}} = (2t - 4)\mathbf{i} + (3t^2 + 2ft)\mathbf{j}$

(b) $\dot{\mathbf{r}} = 0 \qquad \Rightarrow 2t - 4 = 0$ and $3t^2 + 2ft = 0$

$\Rightarrow t = 2 \ \therefore\ f = -3$

29 (a) $\dot{\mathbf{r}} = (2 - 6t)\,\mathbf{i} + 4t\,\mathbf{j}$

$\therefore\quad t = 2 \Rightarrow \dot{\mathbf{r}} = -10\mathbf{i} + 8\mathbf{j}$

(b) $\sqrt{-10^2 + 8} = \sqrt{164}\ \text{m s}^{-1}$

Section 2

1

				Total
Mass (kg)	1	4	8	13
Distance from A	2	9	5	x

$\therefore\ 1 \times 2 + 4 \times 9 + 8 \times 5 = 13\bar{x}\ \therefore\ \bar{x} = 6$ m

2

				Total
Mass (kg)	4	1	5	10
Distance from A	0	24	40	$\bar{x}$

$\therefore\ 4 \times 0 + 1 \times 24 + 5 \times 40 = 10\bar{x}\ \therefore\ \bar{x} = 22.4$ cm

3 $\quad 5 \times -4 + 3 \times 1 + 2 \times 3 = 10\bar{x}\ \therefore\ \bar{x} = -1.1$

4 $\quad \pi \times 5^2 \times 0 + 2 \times \pi \times 5 \times 9 \times 4.5 = 115\pi\bar{y}$

$\therefore\ \bar{y} = 3.52$ cm (2 d.p.)

5 $\quad 80 \times 5 + 24 \times 12 = 104 \times \bar{y}$

$\therefore\ \bar{y} = 6.62$ cm (2 d.p.)

6 $\quad 144 \times 9 - 16\pi \times 14 = (144 - 16\pi)\bar{y}$

$\therefore\ \bar{y} = 6.32$ cm (2 d.p.)

7 (a) $8000 \times 10 + 1000 \times 25 = 9000\bar{y}$

$\therefore\ \bar{y} = 11.67$ mm (2 d.p.)

(In this case, use *volumes* to represent the mass.)

(b) $16\pi \times 0.5 + 9\pi \times 1.5 + 4\pi \times 2.5 + \pi \times 3.5 = 30\pi \times \bar{y}$

$\therefore\ \bar{y} = 1\frac{1}{6}$ cm above the base

8

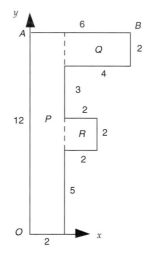

Separate into shapes P, Q and R as shown

	R +	Q +	R =	F–shape
Area	24	8	4	36
x-coordinate	1	4	3	$\bar{x}$
y-coordinate	6	11	6	$\bar{y}$

$\therefore\ 24 \times 1 + 8 \times 4 + 4 \times 3 = 36\bar{x}\ \therefore\ \bar{x} = 1\frac{8}{9}$ cm

$\therefore\ 24 \times 6 + 8 \times 11 + 4 \times 6 = 36\bar{y}\ \therefore\ \bar{y} = 7\frac{1}{9}$ cm

9

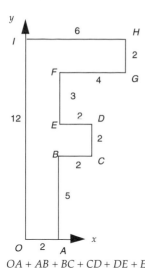

$OA + AB + BC + CD + DE + EF + FG + GH + HI + IO =$ Whole thing.

These are set out in the table below.

Length	2	5	2	2	2	3	4	2	6	12	40
x-coord	1	2	3	4	3	2	4	6	3	0	$\bar{x}$
y-coord	0	2.5	5	6	7	8.5	10	11	12	6	$\bar{y}$

$\therefore \ \bar{x} = 2\frac{1}{10}, \ \bar{y} = 7$

10

	Rectangle	centre hole	end hole	= wanted shape
Area	4000	100π	100π	$4000 - 200\pi$
x-coordinate	50	50	90	$\bar{x}$
y-coordinate	20	20	20	$\bar{y}$

$\therefore \ 4000 \times 50 - 100\pi \times 50 - 100\pi \times 90 =$
$(4000 - 200\pi)\bar{x}$

$\therefore \ \bar{x} = 46.27 \ (2 \text{ d.p.}), \ \bar{y} = 20$

11

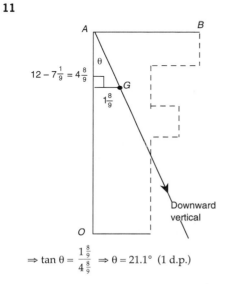

$\Rightarrow \tan\theta = \dfrac{1\frac{8}{9}}{4\frac{8}{9}} \ \Rightarrow \ \theta = 21.1° \ (1 \text{ d.p.})$

12

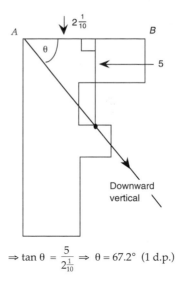

$\Rightarrow \tan\theta = \dfrac{5}{2\frac{1}{10}} \ \Rightarrow \ \theta = 67.2° \ (1 \text{ d.p.})$

13

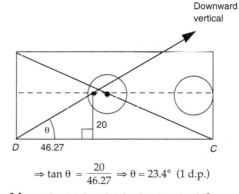

$\Rightarrow \tan\theta = \dfrac{20}{46.27} \ \Rightarrow \ \theta = 23.4° \ (1 \text{ d.p.})$

14 $\therefore \ 3 \times 1 + 5 \times -1 + 2 \times 2 + 4 \times -1 = 14\bar{x}$
$\therefore \ \bar{x} = -\frac{1}{7}$

$\therefore \ 3 \times 6 + 5 \times 5 + 2 \times -3 + 4 \times -4 = 14\bar{y}$
$\therefore \ \bar{y} = 1\frac{1}{2}$

15 Take X as the origin and XY extended as the x-axis. The x-coordinate of the shaded area's centre of gravity is $-\frac{4}{9}r$.

Big circle – Small circle = Shaded area

Area	πR^2	πr^2	$\pi(R^2 - r^2)$
x coordinate	0	$R - r$	$-\frac{4}{9}r$

$\therefore \ \pi R^2 \times 0 - \pi r^2(R - r) = \pi(R^2 - r^2) \times -\frac{4}{9}r$

$\therefore \ r = (R + r)\frac{4}{9}$

$\therefore \ 9r = 4R + 4r \ \Rightarrow \ R = \frac{5}{4}r$

16 (a) 2 cm

(b) $16 \times 2 - 4 \times 3 = 12d \ \Rightarrow d = 1\frac{2}{3}$ cm

(c) $\tan\theta = \dfrac{1\frac{2}{3}}{2} \ \Rightarrow \ \theta = 40°$

Section 3

1 Gain in K.E. $= \frac{1}{2} \times 8 \times 6^2 - \frac{1}{2} \times 8 \times 4^2 = 80$ J

2 (a) $225 \times 4 + 75 \times 0 = 300u \Rightarrow u = 3$ m s^{-1}

(b) KE before $= \frac{1}{2} \times 225 \times 4^2 = 1800$ J

K.E. after $= \frac{1}{2} \times 300 \times 3^2 = 1350$ J

$\therefore$ Loss of KE $= 450$ J

3 (a) $500 = 100a \Rightarrow a = 5$ m s^{-2}

(b) $v^2 = 2 \times 5 \times 40 \Rightarrow v = 20$ m s^{-1}

(c) $100 \times 20 - 10 \times 35 = 110u$

$\Rightarrow u = 15$ m s^{-1}

(d) $196 = 110a \Rightarrow a = -1.78$ m s^{-2}
(so his retardation is 1.78 m s^{-2})

(e) $v^2 = 15^2 - 2 \times 1.78 \times 36.73 \Rightarrow v = 9.7$ m s^{-1}

(f) $\downarrow : 78.4 = 4.9t^2 \Rightarrow t = 4$ seconds

(g) $\rightarrow: s = 9.7 \times 4 = 38.8$ m

(h)

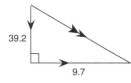

$\therefore$ 40.4 m s^{-1} at 76° to horizontal

(1 d.p. and 2 s.f. respectively)

(i) K.E. before $= \frac{1}{2} \times 100 \times 20^2 + \frac{1}{2} \times 10 \times 35^2 = 26\,125$ J

K.E. after $= \frac{1}{2} \times 110 \times 40.4^2 = 89\,690$ J

$\therefore$ gain in kinetic energy $= 63\,565$ J

(The reason that *K.E. is gained* in this example is that *work is being done*. We shall return to this later.)

Incidentally, you will be pleased to know that the cyclist was also a strong swimmer and successfully swam ashore.

4 (a) Let $u = 21\lambda$ and $v = 26\lambda$

$\therefore 0.08 \times 1.5 + 0.12 \times 1 = 0.08 \times 21\lambda + 0.12 \times 26\lambda$

$\therefore \lambda = 0.05$

$\therefore u = 21\lambda = 1.05$ and $v = 26\lambda = 1.3$

(b) $0.08 \times 1.05 - 0.08 \times 1.5 = $ Impulse

$\therefore$ Impulse $= (-)\, 0.036$ N s.

5 $\frac{1}{2} \times 1000 \times 8^2 = 32\,000$ J or 32 kJ

6 $50 \times 1.65 \times 8 = 660$ J

7 $(40 \times 9.8 \times \sin 60° - 60) \times 10 = \frac{1}{2} \times 40 \times v^2$

$\Rightarrow v = 11.82$ m s^{-1} (2d.p.)

8 $R \times 2.4 = \frac{1}{2} \times 0.01 \times 600^2 \Rightarrow R = 750$ N

9 Component of the weight down the plane $=$ $20 \times 9.8 \times \sin 30°$.

$\therefore 20 \times 9.8 \times \sin 30° \times 5 = \frac{1}{2} \times 20 \times v^2$

$\Rightarrow v = 7$ m s^{-1}

10 Take zero P.E. at the level of the hole H.

$\therefore \frac{1}{2} \times 0.02 \times 3^2 + 0.02 \times 9.8 \times 6 = \frac{1}{2} \times 0.02 \times v^2$

$\Rightarrow v = 11.3$ m s^{-1} (1d.p.).

(Using conservation of energy.)

11 (a) Taking the initial level as zero P.E., the car originally has no total energy. When it reaches B its P.E. is again zero and so it can't have any K.E. there either.

$\therefore$ Car comes to instantaneous rest at B then car does the return journey, just getting back to A. The car continues to oscillate from A to B.

(b) The original energy of the car is now

$\frac{1}{2} \times 1000 \times 6^2 = 18$ kJ.

If it reaches C its potential energy there will be $1000 \times 9.8 \times 10 = 98$ kJ. But the car cannot gain energy and so it cannot reach C.

$\therefore$ Somewhere between B and C the car comes to instantaneous rest. Then the car does the return journey, reappearing at A with a velocity of 6 m s^{-1}.

(c) The original energy of the car is now

$\frac{1}{2} \times 1000 \times 15^2 = 112.5$ kJ.

At C its potential energy would be

$1000 \times 9.8 \times 10 = 98$ kJ

$\therefore$ Its kinetic energy at C will be

112.5 kJ $- 98$ kJ $= 14.5$ kJ

$\therefore 14\,500 = \frac{1}{2} \times 1000 \times u^2 \Rightarrow u = 5.4$ m s^{-1} (1d.p.)

$\therefore$ Car goes over the peak at C with a velocity of 5.4 m s^{-1}. So far so good!

Using conservation of energy at D we get

$\frac{1}{2} \times 1000 \times v^2 - 1000 \times 9.8 \times 5 = 112\,500$

$\Rightarrow v = 18$ m s^{-1} (2 s.f.)

$\therefore$ Car flies off horizontally at D with a velocity of 18 m s^{-1}

$\therefore \rightarrow : 9 = 18t \Rightarrow t = 0.5$

$\therefore$ Car takes 0.5 seconds to cross the gap.

$\therefore \downarrow : s = \frac{1}{2} \times 9.8 \times 0.5^2 \Rightarrow s = 1.225$

$\therefore$ Car drops a vertical distance of 1.225 m in that time. But the actual gap downwards from D to E is 0.5 m.

$\therefore$ The car misses the rail at E and …!

12 $5000 \times 9.8 \times 0.4 = 19.6$ kW

13 Work done on each clay $=$ gain in K.E.

$= 0.5 \times 0.08 \times 20^2 = 16$ J

This occurs in 20 seconds.

$\therefore$ Power into each clay $=$ rate of working per second

$= \frac{16}{20} = 0.8$ W

$\therefore$ Machine power $= 2 \times 0.8 = 1.6$ W

14 120 kg a minute $\Rightarrow$ 2 kg a second.

$10^2 = 2 \times a \times 4 \Rightarrow$ acceleration $= 12.5$ m s^{-2}

Let F be driving force of the fire pump

$\therefore F - 2 \times 9.8 = 2 \times 12.5 \Rightarrow F = 44.6$ N

$\therefore$ Work done by fire pump $= 44.6 \times 4 = 178.4$ J

$\therefore$ Power $= 178.4$ J per second $= 178.4$ W

15 Force down plane $= 800 \times 9.8 \times \frac{1}{10} + 200 = 984$ N

$\therefore$ Power $= 984 \times 20 = 19\,680$ W

16 Inclination of $\sin \theta \left(\frac{1}{14}\right) \Rightarrow$

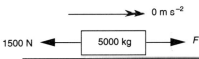

$\Rightarrow \sin \theta = \frac{1}{14}$

Going up the plane: tractive force

$= 200 \times 9.8 \times \frac{1}{14} + k10^2 = 140 + 100k$

Coming down the plane: tractive force

$= -200 \times 9.8 \times \frac{1}{14} + k20^2 = -140 + 400k$

But power developed is the same.

$\therefore (140 + 100k)10 = (-140 + 400k)20$

$\Rightarrow k = 0.6$

$\Rightarrow$ Power $= \left(140 + 100 \times 0.6\right)10 = 2$ kW

17 (a)

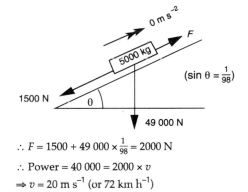

$\therefore F = 1500$ N $\qquad \therefore$ Power $= 40\,000 = 1500 \times v$

$\Rightarrow v = 26\frac{2}{3}$ m s^{-1} (or 96 kmh^{-1})

(b)

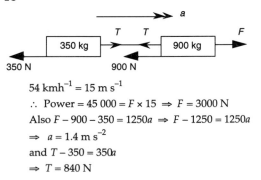

$\therefore F = 1500 + 49\,000 \times \frac{1}{98} = 2000$ N

$\therefore$ Power $= 40\,000 = 2000 \times v$

$\Rightarrow v = 20$ m s^{-1} (or 72 km h^{-1})

18

54 kmh^{-1} = 15 m s^{-1}

$\therefore$ Power $= 45\,000 = F \times 15 \Rightarrow F = 3000$ N

Also $F - 900 - 350 = 1250a \Rightarrow F - 1250 = 1250a$

$\Rightarrow a = 1.4$ m s^{-2}

and $T - 350 = 350a$

$\Rightarrow T = 840$ N

19

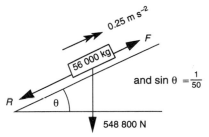

and $\sin \theta = \frac{1}{50}$

Power $= 240\,000 = F \times 5 \Rightarrow F = 48\,000$ N

$\therefore 48\,000 - R - 548\,800 \times \frac{1}{50} = 56\,000 \times 0.25$

$\Rightarrow R = 23\,024$ N

20 (a)

Power $= 400 = F \times 5 \Rightarrow F = 80$ N $\Rightarrow R = 80$ N

(b)

$\therefore F = 110 + 588 \times \frac{1}{12} = 159$ N

$\therefore$ Power $= 400 = 159 \times v$

$\Rightarrow V = 2.52$ m/s (2 d.p.)

(c) Power $= 400 = F \times 2 \Rightarrow F = 200$ N

$\therefore 200 = 110 + 588 \sin \alpha \Rightarrow \alpha = 8.8°$ (1 d.p.)

21

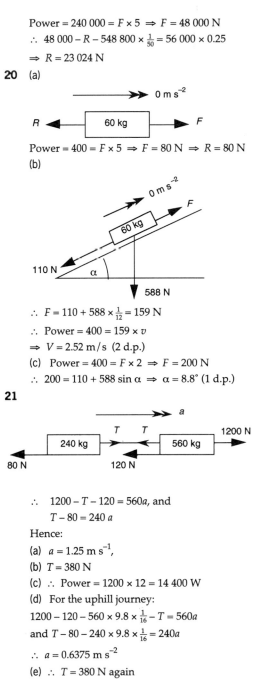

$\therefore 1200 - T - 120 = 560a$, and

$T - 80 = 240a$

Hence:

(a) $a = 1.25$ m s^{-1},

(b) $T = 380$ N

(c) $\therefore$ Power $= 1200 \times 12 = 14\,400$ W

(d) For the uphill journey:

$1200 - 120 - 560 \times 9.8 \times \frac{1}{16} - T = 560a$

and $T - 80 - 240 \times 9.8 \times \frac{1}{16} = 240a$

$\therefore a = 0.6375$ m s^{-2}

(e) $\therefore T = 380$ N again

22 (a)

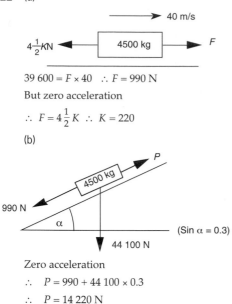

$39\,600 = F \times 40 \quad \therefore F = 990 \text{ N}$

But zero acceleration

$\therefore F = 4\frac{1}{2}K \quad \therefore K = 220$

(b)

$$(\text{Sin } \alpha = 0.3)$$

Zero acceleration

$\therefore P = 990 + 44\,100 \times 0.3$

$\therefore P = 14\,220 \text{ N}$

Same power $\therefore 39\,600 = 14\,220\,v$

$\therefore v = 2.78 \text{ m s}^{-1}$ (2 d.p.)

$\therefore \text{K.E.} = \frac{1}{2} \times 4500 \times 2.78^2 = 17000 \text{ J}$ (2 s.f.)

Section 4

1

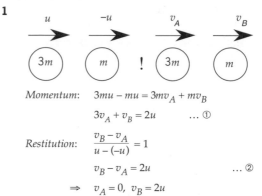

Momentum: $\quad 3mu - mu = 3mv_A + mv_B$

$$3v_A + v_B = 2u \qquad \ldots \text{①}$$

Restitution: $\quad \dfrac{v_B - v_A}{u - (-u)} = 1$

$$v_B - v_A = 2u \qquad\qquad \ldots \text{②}$$

$$\Rightarrow \quad v_A = 0, \ v_B = 2u$$

2 We can call the first sphere A, the second B and take A's initial direction of motion as positive:

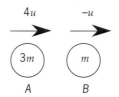

Note that B has a negative velocity since it's moving in the opposite direction to A.

Our two equations for the collision are

Momentum: $\quad 3m \times 4u + m \times (-u)$

$$= 3mv_A + mv_B$$

i.e. $\quad 3v_A + v_B = 11u \qquad\qquad \ldots \text{①}$

Restitution: $\quad \dfrac{v_B - v_A}{4u - (-u)} = e = \dfrac{1}{5}$ (given)

i.e. $\quad v_B - v_A = u \qquad\qquad \ldots \text{②}$

Note that the relative speed before is $5u$ and not $3u$.

Subtracting ② from ①,

$$4v_A = 10u \ \Rightarrow v_A = \frac{5u}{2}$$

and putting this into ②

$$v_B - \frac{5u}{2} = u \ \Rightarrow v_B = \frac{7u}{2}$$

Kinetic energy before, given by $\frac{1}{2}$ mass $\times$ (velocity)^2, is

$$\frac{1}{2}(3m) \times (4u)^2 + \frac{1}{2}(m) \times (-u)^2 = \frac{49mu^2}{2}$$

KE after is $\frac{1}{2}(3m) \times \left(\dfrac{5u}{2}\right)^2 + \frac{1}{2}(m) \times \left(\dfrac{7u}{2}\right)^2$

$$= \frac{75mu^2}{8} + \frac{49mu^2}{8} = \frac{124mu^2}{8} = \frac{31mu^2}{2}$$

Then the loss in kinetic energy is

$$\frac{49mu^2}{2} - \frac{31mu^2}{2} = \frac{18mu^2}{2} = 9mu^2$$

3

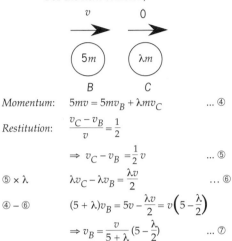

u_A → u_B →

$2m$ (A) $3m$ (B)

Momentum: $2mu_A + 3mu_B = 2mu + 3m\dfrac{3u}{2}$

$$2u_A + 3u_B = \dfrac{13u}{2} \qquad \ldots ①$$

Restitution: $\dfrac{\frac{3u}{2} - u}{u_A - u_B} = \dfrac{1}{5}$

$$\dfrac{u}{2} = \dfrac{1}{5}(u_A - u_B)$$

$$u_A - u_B = \dfrac{5u}{2} \qquad \ldots ②$$

② × 2 $\qquad 2u_A - 2u_B = 5u \qquad \ldots ③$

① − ③ $\qquad 5u_B = \dfrac{3u}{2} \Rightarrow u_B = \dfrac{3u}{10}$

Into ② $\qquad u_A - \dfrac{3u}{10} = \dfrac{5u}{2}$

$\Rightarrow \qquad u_A - \dfrac{28u}{10} = \dfrac{14u}{5}$

Momentum of A: Before $2m \times \dfrac{14u}{5} = \dfrac{28mu}{5}$

After $2mu$

Change is $2mu - \dfrac{28mu}{5} = \dfrac{-18mu}{5}$,
the impulse of B on A (negative because slowed down)

Then the *magnitude* (i.e. ignoring any minus sign)
is $\dfrac{18mu}{5}$

4 (a)

u_A → 0 →

$15m$ (A) $5m$ (B)

Momentum: $\quad 15mu_A = 15mv_A + 5mv \qquad \ldots①$

Restitution: $\quad \dfrac{v - v_A}{u_A} = \dfrac{1}{2} \qquad \ldots②$

① ÷ 5m ÷ $\quad \Rightarrow 3v_A + v = 3u_A \qquad \ldots①'$

② becomes $\quad v - v_A = \dfrac{u_A}{2} \qquad \ldots②'$

②' × 3 $\quad 3v - 3v_A = \dfrac{3u_A}{2} \qquad \ldots③$

①' + ③ $\quad 4v = 3u_A + \dfrac{3u_A}{2} = \dfrac{9u_A}{2}$

$\Rightarrow u_A = \dfrac{8v}{9}$

Into ②', $\quad v - v_A = \dfrac{4v}{9} \Rightarrow v_A = \dfrac{5v}{9}$

(b) (i) $u_A - v_A = \dfrac{3v}{9} = \dfrac{v}{3}$, so change in momentum of A is this × mass,

i.e. $15m \times \dfrac{v}{3} = 5mv$

(ii) The change in momentum of B is equal and opposite to that of A, so in magnitude $5mv$

For the next collision,

v → 0 →

$5m$ (B) λm (C)

Momentum: $\quad 5mv = 5mv_B + \lambda mv_C \qquad \ldots④$

Restitution: $\quad \dfrac{v_C - v_B}{v} = \dfrac{1}{2}$

$\Rightarrow v_C - v_B = \dfrac{1}{2}v \qquad \ldots⑤$

⑤ × λ $\quad \lambda v_C - \lambda v_B = \dfrac{\lambda v}{2} \qquad \ldots⑥$

④ − ⑥ $\quad (5 + \lambda)v_B = 5v - \dfrac{\lambda v}{2} = v\left(5 - \dfrac{\lambda}{2}\right)$

$\Rightarrow v_B = \dfrac{v}{5 + \lambda}\left(5 - \dfrac{\lambda}{2}\right) \qquad \ldots⑦$

If no further collisions, $v_A \leq v_B$

$\Rightarrow \dfrac{5v}{9} \leq \dfrac{v}{5 + \lambda}\left(5 - \dfrac{\lambda}{2}\right)$

$v = 0$ and $\lambda > 0$,

so we can multiply through by $\dfrac{9(5 + \lambda)}{v}$

$5(5 + \lambda) \leq 9\left(5 - \dfrac{\lambda}{2}\right)$

$25 + 5\lambda \leq 45 - \dfrac{9\lambda}{2}$

$5\lambda + \dfrac{9\lambda}{2} \leq 45 - 25 = 20$

$\Rightarrow \dfrac{19\lambda}{2} \leq 20 \Rightarrow \lambda \leq \dfrac{40}{19}$

5 Change in momentum of P is

$m(5u - (-3u)) = 8mu =$ impulse.

Since an equal and opposite impulse acts on Q, it will be $-8mu$.

With a mass of $3m$, this means that it loses $\dfrac{8mu}{3m} = \dfrac{8u}{3}$ in velocity.

$6u - \dfrac{8u}{3} = \dfrac{10u}{3}$, the speed of Q after the collision.

$e = \dfrac{\text{Separation speed}}{\text{Approach speed}} = \dfrac{5u - \frac{10u}{3}}{6u + 3u} = \dfrac{\frac{5u}{3}}{9u}$

$= \dfrac{5}{27}$

$2u$ ← $5u$ ←

m (S) m (P)

Momentum: $2mu + 5mu = mv_S + mv_P$

$$\Rightarrow \quad v_S + v_P = 7u \qquad \ldots \text{①}$$

KE before: $\dfrac{1}{2}m(2u)^2 + \dfrac{1}{2}m(5u)^2 = \dfrac{1}{2}m \times 29u^2$

KE after: $\dfrac{1}{2}mv_S^2 + \dfrac{1}{2}mv_P^2$

$\Rightarrow$ loss: $\dfrac{29}{2}mu^2 - \dfrac{1}{2}mv_S^2 - \dfrac{1}{2}mv_P^2 = 2mu^2$

$$\Rightarrow \quad v_S^2 + v_P^2 = 25u^2 \qquad \ldots \text{②}$$

Rearrange ① $\Rightarrow v_S = 7u - v_P$

into ② $(7u - v_P)^2 + v_P^2 = 25u^2$

$49u^2 - 14v_Pu + v_P^2 + v_P^2 = 25u^2$

$2v_P^2 - 14v_Pu + 24u^2 = 0$

$v_P^2 - 7v_Pu + 12u^2 = 0$

$v_P = 3u \quad \text{or} \quad v_P = 4u$

$v_S = 4u \quad \text{or} \quad v_S = 3u$

But $v_S > v_P \Rightarrow v_P = 3u$

6

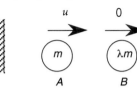

u   0   *m*   *λm*   *A*   *B*

By conservation of momentum:

$$mu = mv_A + \lambda mv_B \qquad \ldots \text{①}$$

By Newton's Experimental Law:

$$\dfrac{v_B - v_A}{u} = e = \dfrac{3}{5} \text{ (given)} \qquad \ldots \text{②}$$

These become: $v_A + \lambda v_B = u \qquad \ldots \text{①'}$

and $v_B - v_A = \dfrac{3u}{5} \qquad \ldots \text{②'}$

Adding these $v_B(1 + \lambda) = \dfrac{8u}{5}$

i.e. $v_B = \dfrac{8u}{5(1 + \lambda)} \qquad \ldots \text{③}$

and putting this into ②'

$$\dfrac{8u}{5(1 + \lambda)} - v_A = \dfrac{3u}{5}$$

$$v_A = \dfrac{8u}{5(1 + \lambda)} - \dfrac{3u}{5} = \dfrac{u}{5}\left[\dfrac{8}{1 + \lambda} - 3\right]$$

$$= \dfrac{u}{5}\left[\dfrac{8 - 3(1 + \lambda)}{1 + \lambda}\right] = \dfrac{u}{5}\left[\dfrac{5 - 3\lambda}{1 + \lambda}\right] \quad \ldots \text{④}$$

If the direction of v_A is to be reversed,
we need this last expression for v_A to be negative, i.e.

$$\dfrac{u}{5}\left[\dfrac{5 - 3\lambda}{1 + \lambda}\right] < 0$$

since u and λ are positive, this is the same as

$$5 - 3\lambda < 0 \Rightarrow \lambda > \dfrac{5}{3} \text{ as required}$$

After collision with the wall, the new velocity of A, which we can call $v^1{}_A$,
will be $-ev_A$, i.e.

$$v^1{}_A = \dfrac{-e}{5}\left[u\left(\dfrac{5 - 3\lambda}{1 + \lambda}\right)\right]$$

$$= \dfrac{3u}{25}\left(\dfrac{3\lambda - 5}{\lambda + 1}\right)$$

reversing and substituting $e = \dfrac{3}{5}$.

If this velocity is greater than v_B, sphere A will catch up with sphere B, i.e. if

$$\dfrac{3u}{25}\left(\dfrac{3\lambda - 5}{\lambda + 1}\right) > \dfrac{8u}{5(\lambda + 1)} \text{ (from ③)}$$

(we can cancel since u and $\lambda + 1$ are greater than zero)

$$\dfrac{3}{5}(3\lambda - 5) > 8 \Rightarrow 3(3\lambda - 5) > 40$$

$$9\lambda - 15 > 40 \Rightarrow 9\lambda > 55$$

$$\lambda > \dfrac{55}{9} \text{ as required.}$$

If $\lambda = 15$, $v^1{}_A = \dfrac{3u}{25}\left(\dfrac{40}{16}\right) = \dfrac{3u}{10}$

and $v_B = \dfrac{8u}{5(16)} = \dfrac{u}{10}$

$\dfrac{3u}{10}$ $\dfrac{u}{10}$ *m*   *15m*   *A*   *B*

Momentum: $\dfrac{3mu}{10} + \dfrac{15mu}{10}$

$$= mw_A + 15mw_B \qquad \ldots \text{⑤}$$

Restitution: $\dfrac{w_B - w_A}{\dfrac{3u}{10} - \dfrac{u}{10}} = \dfrac{3}{5} \qquad \ldots \text{⑥}$

⑥ becomes $w_B - w_A = \dfrac{3}{5}\left(\dfrac{3u}{10} - \dfrac{u}{10}\right) = \dfrac{3u}{25} \qquad \ldots \text{⑦}$

⑤ + ⑦ $16w_B = \dfrac{18u}{10} + \dfrac{3u}{25} = \dfrac{90u + 6u}{50} = \dfrac{48u}{25}$

$\Rightarrow w_B = \dfrac{3u}{25}$ this into ⑦ gives

$$\dfrac{3u}{25} - w_A = \dfrac{3u}{25} \Rightarrow w_A = 0$$

7

u   *eu*   *m*   *em*   *A*   *B*

Momentum: $mu + e^2 mu$

$$= mv_A + emv_B \qquad \ldots \text{①}$$

Restitution: $\dfrac{v_B - v_A}{u - eu} = e$

$$\Rightarrow \quad v_B - v_A = eu(1 - e) \qquad \ldots \text{②}$$

÷ ① by m $\quad v_A + ev_B = u(1+e^2)$ $\qquad$ ... ③

and rearranging

Adding ② + ③

$\quad (1+e)v_B = eu - e^2u + u + e^2u = u(1+e)$

$\Rightarrow \quad v_B = u$

Putting this into ③,

$\quad v_A + eu = u(1+e^2)$

$\Rightarrow \quad v_A = u(1-e+e^2)$

To find a minimum value, we differentiate

$\quad v_A = u(1-e+e^2) \Rightarrow \dfrac{d\,v_A}{de} = u(-1+2e)$

This is zero for a minimum and since
$u \neq 0,\ -1+2e = 0$

(b) $\Rightarrow \quad e = \dfrac{1}{2}$

If $e = \dfrac{1}{2}$, $\qquad v_A = u\left(1 - \dfrac{1}{2} + \dfrac{1}{4}\right) = \dfrac{3u}{4}$

KE before is $\quad \dfrac{1}{2}mu^2 + \dfrac{1}{2}(em)(eu)^2$

KE after is $\quad \dfrac{1}{2}m\left(\dfrac{3u}{4}\right)^2 + \dfrac{1}{2}(em)(u)^2$

Total loss is

$\left[\dfrac{1}{2}mu^2 + \dfrac{1}{2}e^3mu^2\right] - \left[\dfrac{1}{2}m\left(\dfrac{3u}{4}\right)^2 + \dfrac{1}{2}emu^2\right]$

since $e - \dfrac{1}{2}$, this is

$\left[\dfrac{1}{2}mu^2 + \dfrac{mu^2}{16} - \dfrac{9mu^2}{32} - \dfrac{mu^2}{4}\right] = \dfrac{mu^2}{32}$

(c) Momentum of A before was mu

Momentum of A after was $mu(1-e+e^2)$

Change in momentum is

$\quad mu - mu[1-e+e^2] = mu[e-e^2]$

Since impulse is change in momentum,
we want this to be $\dfrac{6}{25}mu$

i.e. $e - e^2 = \dfrac{6}{25} \quad \Rightarrow \quad 25e^2 - 25e + 6 = 0$

$\qquad (5e-2)(5e-3) = 0$

$\qquad \Rightarrow \quad e = \dfrac{2}{5}$ or $e = \dfrac{3}{5}$

8 Since the coefficient of restitution between Q and the barrier is $\dfrac{1}{2}$, it will rebound with speed $\dfrac{1}{2}U$.

KE lost is $\dfrac{1}{2}m(U^2) - \dfrac{1}{2}m\left(\dfrac{1}{2}U^2\right)$

$\quad = \dfrac{1}{2}mU^2\left(1 - \dfrac{1}{4}\right) = \dfrac{3}{8}mU^2$

The momentum of Q just before it collides with P

is $\dfrac{1}{2}mU$.

Then $\quad 4mv_P + mv_Q = \dfrac{1}{2}mU \qquad$ ... ①

$\qquad$ (momentum)

$\dfrac{v_P - v_Q}{\dfrac{1}{2}U} = \dfrac{2}{3} \Rightarrow v_P - v_Q = \dfrac{1}{3}U \qquad$ ...②

$\qquad$ (restitution)

Dividing ① by m and adding,

$\quad 5v_P = \dfrac{5U}{6} \Rightarrow v_P = \dfrac{U}{6}$

Into ②, $\dfrac{U}{6} - v_Q = \dfrac{U}{3}$

$\Rightarrow v_Q = \dfrac{U}{6} - \dfrac{U}{3} = -\dfrac{U}{6}$

i.e. Q rebounds towards the wall. After the third collision, its velocity will be

$\quad \dfrac{1}{2} \times \dfrac{U}{6} = \dfrac{U}{12}$.

This is not enough to catch up with P (velocity $\dfrac{U}{6}$),

so there are three collisions altogether.

Before 2nd collision, KE is $\dfrac{1}{2}m\left(\dfrac{1}{2}U\right)^2$

After 2nd collision, KE is

$\quad \dfrac{1}{2} \times 4m \times \left(\dfrac{1}{6}U\right)^2 + \dfrac{1}{2} \times m \times \left(-\dfrac{1}{6}U\right)^2$

Loss is

$\dfrac{mU^2}{8} - \dfrac{mU^2}{18} - \dfrac{mU^2}{72} - \dfrac{mU^2}{72}[9-4-1] = \dfrac{mU^2}{18}$

Momentum of Q before was $\dfrac{1}{2}mU$

And after was $-\dfrac{1}{6}mU$ so change in momentum

$= \dfrac{1}{2}mU - \left(-\dfrac{1}{6}mU\right) = \dfrac{2}{3}mU$

$=$ the impulse on Q

9 Just before ceiling,

$\uparrow:\quad u \qquad v \qquad a \qquad s \qquad t$

$\qquad U \qquad\qquad -g \qquad \dfrac{h}{2}$

$\Rightarrow v^2 = U^2 - gh$

$\therefore\ v^2 = U^2 - gh \Rightarrow v = \sqrt{U^2 - gh}$

After impact with ceiling, $v = \dfrac{1}{2}\sqrt{U^2 - gh}$ downwards

$\downarrow:\qquad u \qquad v \qquad a \qquad s \qquad t$

$\qquad \dfrac{1}{2}\sqrt{U^2 - gh} \qquad\quad g \qquad h$

$\therefore\ V^2 = \dfrac{1}{4}(U^2 - gh) + 2gh = \dfrac{U^2}{4} + \dfrac{7gh}{4} \quad$ ... ①

After impact with floor, $v = \dfrac{1}{2}\sqrt{\dfrac{U^2}{4} + \dfrac{7gh}{4}}$

Again using $v^2 = u^2 + 2as$,

$0 = \dfrac{1}{4}\left(\dfrac{U^2}{4} + \dfrac{7gh}{4}\right) - 2gh$

$8gh = \dfrac{U^2}{4} + \dfrac{7gh}{4} \Rightarrow \dfrac{U^2}{4} = \dfrac{25gh}{4}$

$\Rightarrow U = 5\sqrt{gh}$

Into ①, $V^2 = \dfrac{25gh}{4} + \dfrac{7gh}{4} = \dfrac{32gh}{4} = 8gh$

$\Rightarrow \quad V = \sqrt{8gh}$

Just before ceiling, $v = -\sqrt{25gh - gh}$

$= -\sqrt{24gh}$

Just after, $v = +\frac{1}{2}\sqrt{24gh}$

$\Rightarrow$ impulse is $\frac{3}{2}m\sqrt{24gh}$

Just before floor, $v = \sqrt{8gh}$

Just after, $v = -\frac{1}{2}\sqrt{8gh}$

$\Rightarrow$ impulse is $\frac{3}{2}m\sqrt{8gh}$

$\Rightarrow$ ratio ceiling : floor is

$\frac{3}{2}m\sqrt{24gh} : \frac{3}{2}m\sqrt{8gh} \quad \Rightarrow \sqrt{3} : 1$

Section 5

1   (a)   We saw in Section 2 that the centre of mass G of a triangular lamina is $\frac{1}{3}$ of the way up any median.

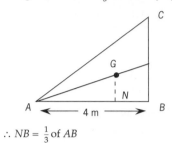

$\therefore NB = \frac{1}{3}$ of AB

$\therefore NB = \frac{4}{3}$ m $\therefore AN = \frac{8}{3}$ m

(b)   The force diagram is therefore:

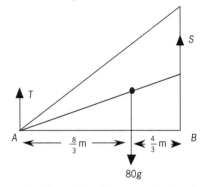

The vertical forces T and S have to be found.

Resolving $\uparrow$: $T + S = 80g$

$A \circlearrowleft$: $80g \times \frac{8}{3} = S \times 4$

Solve these to get $S = 522\frac{2}{3}$ N and $T = 261\frac{1}{3}$ N

2   The force diagram is

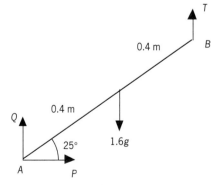

We have to find: the forces P and Q at A
                              the tension T

Resolving $\uparrow$: $T + Q = 1.6g$

Resolving $\rightarrow$: $P = 0$

$A \circlearrowleft$: $1.6g \, . \, 0.4 \cos 25° = T \times 0.8 \cos 25°$

Solve the equations to get

$T = 0.8$ g $= 7.84$ N, $Q = 0.8g = 7.84$ N, and $P = 0$

The required solution is therefore:

3 The force diagram is:

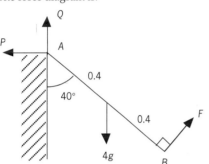

(a) We have to find: the force F
the force P and Q at A

Resolving $\uparrow$: $Q + F\cos 50° = 4g$

Resolving $\rightarrow$: $P = F\cos 40°$

A$\circlearrowright$: $F . 0.8 = 4g . 0.4 \sin 40°$

Solve then to get

$F \sim 12.6$ N, $P \sim 9.7$ N and $Q \sim 31.1$ N

(b) The required solution is therefore:

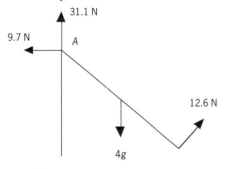

4 (a) $Q\circlearrowright$: $P . 1.4 = 150 . 0.4$ ∴ $P = 42.86$ N

∴ Force at P is 42.86 N towards the door and force at Q is 42.86 N away from the door.

(b) $Q\circlearrowright$: $150 . 0.4 = F . 0.8$ ∴ $F = 75$ N

The force F is 75 N.

5

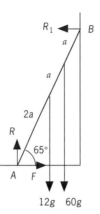

Let the ladder AB have length $4a$. We have to find forces R_1 and R.

Resolving $\uparrow$: $R = 72g$

Resolving $\rightarrow$: $F = R_1$

A$\circlearrowright$: $12g . 2a \cos 65° + 60g . 3a \cos 65° = R_1 . 4a \sin 65°$

Solve these equations to get

$R_1 \sim 233$ N, $F = 233$ N and $r = 705.6$ N

The required solutions is therefore:

(a) 233 N away from the wall

(b) 233 N horizontally and 705.6 N vertically